チェアーサイドの歯科英会話

外国人患者が診療所を訪れたら

Dental Chairside Communication in English and Japanese

監修
加藤有三（長崎大学名誉教授）

編集
吉田教明
澤瀬　隆
渡邊郁哉
ルール ドーン ミシェル

執筆
鮎瀬　卓郎（長崎大学大学院医歯薬学総合研究科 歯科麻酔学 教授）
池田　　毅（長崎大学病院 臨床教授）
石飛　進吾（元 長崎大学病院 口腔ケア・摂食・嚥下リハビリテーションセンター 講師）
久保　至誠（前 長崎大学病院 保存修復学部門 准教授）
齋藤　俊行（元 長崎大学大学院医歯薬学総合研究科 口腔保健学 教授）
澤瀬　　隆（長崎大学大学院医歯薬学総合研究科 口腔インプラント学 教授）
平　　曜輔（同 歯科補綴学 准教授）
日髙　　聖（同 小児歯科学 助教）
藤井　哲則（前 長崎大学病院 医療教育開発センター 講師）
佛坂　斉祉（長崎大学大学院医歯薬学総合研究科 歯科矯正学 准教授）
吉田　教明（同 歯科矯正学 教授）
吉田　治志（前 長崎大学病院 特殊歯科総合治療部 准教授）
吉村　篤利（長崎大学大学院医歯薬学総合研究科 歯周歯内治療学 准教授）
渡邊　郁哉（同 生体材料学 教授）
ルール ドーン ミシェル（長崎大学 言語教育研究センター 講師）

医歯薬出版株式会社

付属音声ナレーション
ルール ドーン ミシェル　　長崎大学 言語教育研究センター 講師
ディビッド アトウッド　　長崎南山学園 教諭
渡邊　有里彩　　長崎大学附属中学校

イラスト
Indy yutaka

序　文

　長崎大学歯学部において学部学生の講義に用いられた英会話の講義録が,「チェアーサイドの歯科英会話」のタイトルで出版されるまでに熟成してきたことを,その授業開設を準備した関係者の一人として心から喜んでおります.

　近年の高等教育においては,国際人として必要な英語によるコミュニケーション能力を身につけることが求められてきています.日本人の学生が将来留学する機会に恵まれた場合にはもちろん国際的に通用する英語力が必須です.また,国内で歯科医療に従事する場合においても,年々増加する外国人に対し,安心・安全な医療を提供するための異文化間コミュニケーション能力を向上させることが不可欠となっています.

　従来から,歯科医師および歯科衛生士のための英会話については,数種の本がすでに発刊されております.一般の英会話の本とは異なる今回のこの教科書の特徴は,各診療科において日常の診療業務の中心にいる教員の内で,数年間の海外研修を経験した人達のボランティアによって作りだされたということです.まず,それぞれの専門分野の診療を想定し,日本語での状況設定がなされました.次にネイティブスピーカーとの間で英会話テキストの推敲が繰り返されました.長崎大学歯学部では,当初5年生のための選択科目として採用しました.前,後期それぞれ10回を1セットとして開講し,2年間にわたって修正を加えながら会話教室で使った結果,ここに出版するに至ったものです.

　当初は,日本語に不慣れな外国人の患者さんが来院したときのための,基本的な臨床英会話のみに用いる目的でしたが,本格的な歯科臨床をこれから開始しようとする学生諸君にとっては,日本人の患者さんとの会話としても十分役立つものとなっています.大学では患者さんと歯科医師の間の会話を教育する科目は従来から十分には準備されていませんでしたが,この本に示すような英会話を通じて,英語ばかりでなく日本語の会話の大切さも同様に学ぶことになるのではないかと思います.

　最後に,この本が歯科診療室で先生方の役に立つことを夢見ながら,この会話集の完成に協力された諸先生方の努力に対して,深甚なる敬意を表し,序文のご挨拶といたします.

平成23年3月吉日

長崎大学名誉教授　加　藤　有　三

音声データのダウンロードとご利用について

下記の URL または QR コードから無料でダウンロードすることができます．
https://www.ishiyaku.co.jp/apde/423380/

＜注意事項＞
・再生には MP3 形式の音声データを再生できるプレイヤーが必要です．
・お客様がご負担になる通信料金について十分にご理解のうえご利用をお願いします．
・音声データを無断で複製・公に上映・公衆送信（送信可能化を含む）・翻訳・翻案することは法律により禁止されています．

＜お問合せ先＞
https://www.ishiyaku.co.jp/ebooks/inquiry/

目　次

レッスン1　初　診 ………… 藤井哲則…2
　受付・初診時　2
　治療終了　2
　全身的な既往歴　4
　その他の事項　6
　エックス線検査　6
　デンタルエックス線写真撮影　8
　パノラマエックス線写真撮影　8

レッスン2　保存処置 ……… 久保至誠…10
　知覚過敏処置　10
　修復処置　10
　覆髄法　12
　抜髄　14
　感染根管治療　14

レッスン3　歯周治療 ……… 吉村篤利…16
　歯肉炎　16
　歯周炎　18
　急性歯周膿瘍　18

レッスン4　クラウン・ブリッジによる
補綴処置 ………………… 平　曜輔…22
　クラウンによる補綴処置　22

　初診日　22
　支台築造のための形成・印象　22
　クラウンのための支台歯形成　24
　印象，咬合採得，色調採得　24
　受付にて　26
　クラウンの装着　26
　ブリッジによる補綴処置　28

　初診日　28
　ブリッジの装着後　28

Lesson 1　FIRST VISIT ………………3
　RECEPTION-FIRST VISIT　3
　AFTER TREATMENT　3
　GENERAL HISTORY　5
　OTHER ISSUES　7
　X-RAY EXAMINATION　7
　DENTAL X-RAY　9
　PANORAMIC RADIOGRAPHY　9

Lesson 2　ENDODONTICS & OPERATIVE DENTISTY ………………………11
　HYPERSENSITIVITY OF TEETH　11
　RESTORATION　11
　PULP CAPPING　13
　PULP EXTIRPATION　15
　ROOT CANAL TREATMENT　15

Lesson 3　PERIODONTAL TREATMENT ……………………………………17
　GINGIVITIS　17
　PERIODONTITIS　19
　ACUTE PERIODONTAL ABSCESS　21

Lesson 4　PROSTHODONTIC TREATMENT USING CROWN & BRIDGE… 23
PROSTHODONTIC TREATMENT USING A CROWN　23
　THE FIRST VISIT　23
　PREPARATION AND IMPRESSION FOR A POST CORE　23
　TOOTH PREPARATION FOR A CROWN　25
　TAKING IMPRESSIONS, BITE REGISTRATION, AND SHADE　25
　AT THE RECEPTION DESK　27
　FIXING THE CROWN　27
PROSTHODONTIC TREATMENT USING A FIXED PARTIAL DENTURE (BRIDGE)　29
　THE FIRST VISIT　29
　FIXING THE BRIDGE　29

レッスン5　インプラント治療 ……………………………… 澤瀬　隆…32	Lesson 5　IMPLANT THERAPY … 33
レッスン6　可撤性義歯による処置 ……………………………… 藤井哲則…36 義歯の不適合　36 義歯の破折　36 新しい義歯の製作　38	Lesson 6　REMOVABLE PROSTHO-DONTIC TREATMENT ……………… 37 POORLY-FITTING DENTURES　37 BREAKAGE OF DENTURES　37 NEW DENTURES　39
レッスン7　歯科予防処置（ケア） ……………………………… 齋藤俊行…42 口臭予防　42 フッ化物による予防処置　44 ブラッシング指導　46	Lesson 7　PREVENTIVE DENTIS-TRY ……………………………………… 43 PREVENTION OF HALITOSIS　43 FLUORIDE APPLICATION　45 INSTRUCTIONS FOR TOOTHBRUSHING　47
レッスン8　小児への処置 ……………………………… 日髙　聖…52 はじめまして　52 口腔内診査　52 局所麻酔　52 治療に取りかかる　54 保護者への説明　56	Lesson 8　TREATMENT FOR A CHILD ……………………………………… 53 THE FIRST VISIT　53 ORAL EXAMINATION　53 PAIN-KILLER SHOT　53 FIXING THE TEETH　55 EXPLANATION TO THE PARENT　57
レッスン9　矯正処置 ……………………… 吉田教明，佛坂斉祉…60 相談・初診時　60 検査　62 診断　62	Lesson 9　ORTHODONTIC TREAT-MENT ……………………………………… 61 CONSULTATION・FIRST VISIT　61 EXAMINATION　63 DIAGNOSIS　63
レッスン10　審美歯科 ……… 池田　毅…66 ホワイトニング　66 失活歯の漂白　66 オフィスホワイトニングとホームホワイトニング　66 ポーセレンラミネートベニア修復　72 初診日　72 支台歯形成，色調採得，印象　72 ラミネートベニアの装着　72	Lesson 10 ESTHETIC DENTISTRY ……………………………………………… 67 WHITENING　67 WHITENING NON-VITAL TEETH　67 IN-OFFICE WHITENING AND HOME WHITENING　67 PROSTHODONTIC TREATMENT USING PORCELAIN LAMINATE VENEER　73 THE FIRST VISIT　73 TOOTH PREPARATION, SHADE TAKING, AND IMPRESSION　73 FIX THE LAMINATE VENEER　73

レッスン11　顎関節症　………　藤井哲則…76	Lesson 11　TEMPOROMANDIBULAR JOINT DISORDERS……………………77
レッスン12　摂食嚥下リハビリテーション　………………　石飛進吾…80	Lesson 12　DYSPHAGIA REHABILI-TATION……………………………………81
問診　80	CONSULTATION　81
診査　80	EXAMINATION　81
検査　80	TEST　81
診断と説明　82	DIAGNOSIS AND EXPLANATION　83
対処法　82	TREATMENT　83
レッスン13　特殊な歯科治療　………………　吉田治志…84	Lesson 13　SPECIAL TREATMENT……………………………………………85
診査　84	EXAMINATION　85
レッスン14　口腔外科と歯科麻酔処置　………………　鮎瀬卓郎…88	Lesson 14　ORAL SURGICAL TREAT-MENT & DENTAL ANESTHESIA…89
外傷　88	AN INJURY　89
智歯周囲炎　88	PERICORONITIS OF THE WISDOM TOOTH　89
抜歯　90	TOOTH EXTRACTION　91
局麻時の不快症状とその対応　92	DISCOMFORT EPISODE DURING DENTAL TREATMENT AND EFFECTIVE TREATMENT　93
救急処置（一次救命処置）　96	BASIC LIFE SUPPORT（BLS）　97

アメリカの歯科事情　………　渡邊郁哉
1 医療費と保険制度　8　　2 インプラント治療　34
3 歯科検診と予防　50　　4 歯科検診システム　58
5 歯科専門医制度　64　　6 審美歯科　70
7 口腔外科専門医養成制度　96

付録　国際的視野を持つ歯科医療人育成に必要な討議を英語で収録　98	Chairside Communication Discussion Questions　98

チェアーサイドの歯科英会話
外国人患者が診療所を訪れたら

Dental Chairside Communication in English and Japanese

レッスン1　初　診

○ **受付・初診時**

患　者　こちらで歯の治療を受けたいのですが．
受　付　初めてですか？
患　者　初めてです．
受　付　紹介状をお持ちですか？
患　者　ええ，持っています．
受　付　保険証をお持ちですか？
患　者　はい，これです．
受　付　見せていただいていいですか？
　　　　この病院は予約制です．
　　　　今日は少し混んでいますので，
　　　　応急処置になると思います．
　　　　お時間は大丈夫ですか？
　　　　20分くらいかかりますが．
患　者　大丈夫です．
歯科医　スミスさんお入りください．
　　　　10番のイスに座ってください．

○ **治療終了後**

受　付　いかがでしたか？
患　者　はい，大丈夫です．
受　付　気分はわるくないですか？
患　者　ええ，大丈夫です．
受　付　これがあなたの診察券です．
　　　　次回から，これを受付に出してください．
　　　　紛失した場合は，言ってください．
　　　　再発行します．
　　　　では，次回の予約をしましょう．
　　　　どの日が都合がいいですか？
患　者　ええと，来週の月曜日がいいです．
受　付　午前中では11時，午後では5時と6時が空いています．
　　　　いかがでしょうか？
患　者　では6時なら大丈夫と思います．
受　付　もし，予約を変更されるときには早めにお電話ください．

LESSON 1 FIRST VISIT

○ RECEPTION - FIRST VISIT

Patient   I would like to have a check up.

Receptionist   Is this your first visit?

Patient   Yes, it is.

Recept.   Do you have a letter of introduction?

Patient   Yes, I do.

Recept.   Do you have a Japanese National Health Insurance card?

Patient   Yes, I do. Here it is.

Recept.   Great, can I see it?

   This clinic has an appointment system.

   Since we are busy today, the dentist will give you like a little routine check up.

   Do you have enough time?

   It'll take about twenty minutes.

Patient   Sure. No problem.

Dentist   Miss Smith. Please come in.

   Have a seat in chair No.10.

○ AFTER TREATMENT

Recept.   Was it all right?

Patient   It was OK. No problem.

Recept.   Do you feel OK now?

Patient   So, so, OK I guess.

Recept.   This is your patient card.

   Please show it to the reception counter every time you come.

   If you lose this card, please tell us.

   We can make a new one.

   Now, would you like to make your next appointment?

   When is the most convenient day for you?

Patient   Let's see. Next Monday looks good.

Recept.   We have free time at eleven a.m., at five p.m. and six p.m.

   And you?

Patient   Well, I guess six p.m. is OK.

Recept.   If you want to change your appointment, please call us as soon as possible.

そのとき担当医の名前をおっしゃってください．
あなたの担当医は加藤です．
今日の料金は 1,200 円です．
お釣りです．確かめてください．
お大事に．
患　者　ありがとう．

○全身的な既往歴

歯科医　すこしお身体についてお尋ねします．
今までに大きな病気をしたことがありますか？
たとえば，心臓病，肝臓病や腎臓病などです．
患　者　いいえ，したことがありません．
歯科医　たとえば卵，牛乳や魚など食べ物で
アレルギー反応がありますか？
患　者　貝とサバでアレルギーがあります．
歯科医　わかりました．薬や注射でアレル
ギーや副作用を起こしたことがあ
りますか？たとえば，鎮痛剤，ペニシ
リンやほかの抗生物質などです．
患　者　ありません．
歯科医　今ほかの病院にかかっていますか？
たとえば，高血圧，更年期障害や片
頭痛などです．

患　者　はい，かかっています．
歯科医　それはどんな病気ですか？
患　者　喘息（ぜんそく）です．
　　　　2 年間中央病院で治療を受けています．
歯科医　飲んでいる薬はありますか？　たとえば，痛み止めや風邪薬です．
患　者　はい，鎮痛剤を飲んでいます．
歯科医　その薬は何ですか？
患　者　セデスです．
歯科医　貧血で治療を受けたことがありますか？
患　者　いいえ，ありません．
歯科医　痙攣の発作を起こしたことがありますか？
患　者　ありません．
歯科医　局所麻酔で気分がわるくなったことがありますか？

	Please tell us your dentist's name at that time.
	Dr. Katou is your dentist.
	Today's consultation is 1,200 yen.
	Here is your change. Please make sure it's right.
	See you next time.
Patient	Thank you very much.

◯ GENERAL HISTORY

Dentist	I'd like to ask you about your general history.
	Have you ever had a serious illness?
	For example heart disease, liver disease or kidney disease?
Patient	No. Nothing.
Dentist	Do you have any allergies?
	For example eggs, milk or fish.
Patient	I'm allergic to shellfish and mackerels.
Dentist	OK.
	Have you ever had any allergic reactions or side effects to medicines or injections?
	For example, painkillers, penicillin, or other antibiotics.
Patient	No, I haven't.
Dentist	Are you receiving any medical treatment now?
	For example, for high blood pressure, menopause or migraine.
Patient	Yes, I am.
Dentist	What kind of illness is it?
Patient	I have asthma.
	I have been treated in Central hospital for two years.
Dentist	Are you taking any drugs? For example painkillers or cold medicines.
Patient	Yes, I am taking over the counter painkillers.
Dentist	OK. What's the name?
Patient	Cedes.
Dentist	OK. Have you ever been treated for anemia?
Patient	No, I haven't.
Dentist	Have you ever suffered from epilepsy?
Patient	No, I haven't.
Dentist	Do you feel sick if you have a local anesthetic?

患者　いいえ，ありません．
歯科医　お酒はよく飲みますか？たとえば焼酎やウイスキーなど強いお酒は麻酔の効果に影響を及ぼすからです．
患者　ビールを毎日飲んでいます．
歯科医　そうですか．血圧は高いほうですか？
患者　いいえ．
歯科医　歯を抜いたことがありますか？たとえば親知らずです．
患者　はい，あります．
歯科医　長く出血しませんでしたか？
患者　いいえ，出血はすぐ止まりました．
歯科医　今，風邪をひいていますか？
患者　いいえ，ひいていません．
歯科医　糖尿病ではありませんか？
患者　いいえ，しかし家族には糖尿病の者がいました．

○ その他の事項
歯科医　ところで，ここまで通院できますか？
　　　　どちらで仕事はされていますか？
患者　ええ，この近くで仕事をしています．
歯科医　あなたの治療には5回通院が必要です．
　　　　しかし，アメリカで治療すれば3回で終わるかもしれません．
　　　　3回の治療では痛みが出るかもしれませんし，私は急いで治療したくありません．
　　　　まあでも，なんとか早く終わるようにしましょう．
　　　　それで，なんとか頑張って4回にしましょう．
　　　　それで，いいですか？
患者　いいです．治療は保険でできますか？
歯科医　はい，できます．

○ エックス線検査
歯科医　レントゲンを撮りましょう．
　　　　妊娠していませんか？
　　　　1階にある放射線科に行ってください．
　　　　放射線科の受付にこの伝票を出してください．

Patient	No, I don't.
Dentist	Do you drink a lot of alcohol?
	For example, shouchu or whiskey because it affects the effect of local anesthetic.
Patient	I drink beer every day.
Dentist	Uh-huh, I see. Have you ever had high blood pressure?
Patient	No, I haven't.
Dentist	Have you ever had a tooth extracted?
	For example wisdom teeth.
Patient	Yes, I have.
Dentist	Was there excessive bleeding?
Patient	No. I don't think so.
Dentist	Do you have a cold now?
Patient	No, I don't.
Dentist	Are you diabetic?
Patient	No, but there was a history of diabetes in my family.

○ OTHER ISSUES

Dentist	By the way, is it convenient for you to come here?
	Where do you work?
Patient	Yeah, I work near here.
Dentist	OK. This treatment usually takes five visits.
	But in the US this same treatment may take only three times.
	You may feel pain after three times treatments, and I don't like to rush through a treatment.
	But let's try to do this treatment as quickly as we can.
	If it goes well we may finish in four visits instead of five.
	All right?
Patient	Yes, it's OK. This treatment will be covered by my insurance, right?
Dentist	Yes. That's no problem.

○ X-RAY EXAMINATION

Dentist	I'd like to take an X-ray.
	Are you pregnant?
	Please go to the radiologic department on the first floor.
	Just show this slip to the reception counter.

さあ，どうぞ，またここに戻ってください．

◯デンタルエックス線写真撮影
技　師　では，ここに座ってください．
　　　　頭を後ろにつけて，口を開けてください．
　　　　フィルムを口の中に入れます．
　　　　右手の人差指でフィルムをしっかり押さえてください．
　　　　はい，いいです．

◯パノラマエックス線写真撮影
技　師　口の周り全体のレントゲンを撮ります．
　　　　ここに顎をのせて，額を前につけてください．
　　　　はい，いいですか？
　　　　機械があなたの頭の周りを回ります．
　　　　リラックスしてください．

アメリカの歯科事情 1　－医療費と保険制度－

アメリカの歯科医療は自由診療で，各歯科医院で治療費を決めています．その治療費は高額なので，国民皆保険制度ではないアメリカでは，治療を受けたくても，受けられない人が大勢います．これは歯科に限ったことではなく，たとえば交通事故にあって重症な状態で近くの病院に運ばれても，保険に加入していなかったり，加入している保険のランクが低かったりすると，治療を拒否されることがあります．一応，老齢者を対象としたメディケア，および低所得者向けのメディケイドという公的な制度はありますが，民間の保険に比べると程度の低い保険です．歯科でも患者は民間の保険会社から歯科保険を買うわけですが，保険会社によって種類も異なり，掛け金によりランクがいくつかあります．それは定期検査（エックス線検査を含む）やクリーニングなどの予防処置だけをカバーするもの（Preventive）や，治療の一部（Standard）やほとんど（Premium）をカバーするものもあります．

OK. Here you go, Finally, please come back here.

DENTAL X-RAY

Technician OK. Please sit down.
Please place the back of your head here and open your mouth.
Please place your right forefinger here to hold the film steady.
That's fine.

PANORAMIC RADIOGRAPHY

Technician I'll take an X-ray of your whole mouth.
Please rest your chin on here and rest your forehead here.
OK, ready?
The machine is going to move all around your head.
Just, relax, and take it easy.

レッスン2　保存処置

○ 知覚過敏処置

患　者　ときどき，歯を磨くと痛いのです．
歯科医　どこが痛みますか？
患　者　左上の前歯です．
歯科医　空気を吹きかけるとしみますか？
患　者　はい．
歯科医　歯茎が下がって根っこが出て，少し削れています．それで，しみるようになったのですよ．露出しているところを薬でコーティングするか，削れているところを詰めればいいでしょう．痛みがとれないときには，神経を取ります．
　　　　まずは薬を塗ってみましょうか．いいですか？
患　者　お願いします．
歯科医　どうですか．
患　者　まだ少しはしみますが，前よりはいいです．
歯科医　歯の磨き方がわるいと，歯茎が下がります．今から磨き方を教えます．

○ 修復処置

歯科医　今日はどうされましたか？
患　者　詰めた物が外れました．
歯科医　それはいけませんね．どの歯から外れましたか？
患　者　右下の奥歯です．
歯科医　いつ外れましたか？
患　者　2日前，飴を食べていたら外れました．
歯科医　歯は痛くないですか？
患　者　痛くありません．
歯科医　冷たい物や熱い物はしみませんか？
患　者　冷たい物が少ししみますが，普段は痛くありません．
歯科医　その歯を何年前に治療したか，覚えていますか．
患　者　よく覚えてないけど，5, 6年前だと思います．
歯科医　外れた物は持って来ましたか？
患　者　はい．

LESSON 2 ENDODONTICS & OPERATIVE DENTISTRY

○ HYPERSENSITY OF TEETH

Patient	Sometimes tooth brushing is painful.
Dentist	Which tooth is sensitive?
Patient	Left upper front tooth.
Dentist	Does air feel painful?
Patient	Yes, it does.
Dentist	The gum recedes and the root surface becomes exposed and a little abraded.
	These sometimes cause hypersensitivity.
	In your case, a coating of medicine or filling in your abrasion will take care of the problem.
	If the pain doesn't stop, taking out the tooth nerve may be necessary.
	Well, let's coat the teeth. Ready?
Patient	OK.
Dentist	Do you feel any pain?
Patient	I feel a slight pain, but it's better than before.
Dentist	Incorrect tooth brushing causes gum recession.
	So, I'll teach you how to use a toothbrush.

○ RESTORATION

Dentist	Hi! What's the trouble?
Patient	My metal filling came out.
Dentist	That sounds terrible. From which tooth?
Patient	It's the lower back right tooth.
Dentist	When did the filling fall out?
Patient	Two days ago, when I was eating some candies.
Dentist	Is it painful?
Patient	No not really.
Dentist	Is it sensitive to cold or hot drinks?
Patient	It is a bit sensitive to cold water. But, I don't feel a constant pain.
Dentist	When was this tooth treated?
Patient	I don't remember well, I think it's five or six years ago now.
Dentist	Did you bring your filling?
Patient	Yes, I did.

保存処置

歯科医　口の中を診せていただきます．イスを倒しますよ．
患　者　はい，わかりました．
歯科医　もう少し，頭のほうに（上に）上がってください．はい，それでいいです．
　　　　それでは（はい），口を開けてください．外れたところにむし歯がありますね．
　　　　こうやっても，痛くないですか？
患　者　痛くありません．
歯科医　こうやっても痛くないですか？
患　者　大丈夫です．

エックス線写真を見せながら

歯科医　詰めた物が外れたのは，セメントが溶けたのが原因です．
　　　　むし歯は神経まで達していないので，神経を取らなくても大丈夫でしょう．
　　　　このまま，これを付けることもできるし，削って詰めなおすこともできます．
　　　　もちろん，隙間があるので削って詰めなおすのがよいと思います．
　　　　どうされますか？
患　者　作りなおしてください．
歯科医　作りなおすには，少し歯を削らなければなりません．
　　　　詰める材料は歯と同じ色のプラスチックでもできます．
　　　　もちろん，プラスチックは金属に比べて弱く，早くすり減ります．
　　　　プラスチックも金属もどちらも保険でできます．
　　　　心配いりません．アマルガムは使いません．どちらにしますか？
患　者　金属でお願いします．
歯科医　今から削りますけど，いいですか？
　　　　痛かったら手を上げてください．
患　者　（左手を上げる．）
歯科医　大丈夫ですか？
　　　　我慢されますか，それとも麻酔をしますか？
患　者　麻酔をしてください．
　　　　麻酔をして大丈夫ですか？
歯科医　ええ，問題ありません．
歯科医　削るのは終わりました．
　　　　これから，型をとります．
　　　　うがいをして待っていてください．

C **覆髄法**

歯科医　かなり深いむし歯です．むし歯が神経の大変近くまで広がっています．
　　　　しかし，神経に炎症が起こっていないようなので，神経を取らないで薬をつけ

Dentist	OK. I'll check the tooth. I'm going to lean the chair back. OK?
Patient	OK, no problem.
Dentist	Please slide up the chair. Good thanks. Perfect.
	Open your mouth, please. There is the cavity.
	Does this hurt your tooth?
Patient	No it doesn't.
Dentist	Does this feel painful?
Patient	It's all right.

In showing X-ray dental film

Dentist	The filling came out because the cement dissolved. The decay hasn't reached the tooth nerve. It'll be all right, I don't have to remove the nerve.
	I can set the filling again or drill and fill it again.
	Of course, drilling and filling it again is the best because there is a crevice between the tooth and the filling. Which do you want to do?
Patient	Make a new one.
Dentist	For making a new one, I guess I'll have to drill a bit.
	The filling material used is a plastic the same color as your teeth.
	Of course, plastic is weaker and more easily worn down than metal.
	Both are covered by insurance. Don't worry, we don't use amalgam.
	Which material would you prefer?
Patient	Please use metal.
Dentist	OK. Now, I'm going to drill. Are you ready?
	If you feel pain, raise your hand, please.
Patient	(patient raises the left hand)
Dentist	Are you OK?
	Can you bear it, or should I use a local anesthetic?
Patient	Please use it.
	Do you mind?
Dentist	Of course not, no problem.
Dentist	I've finished drilling.
	After this, I'm going to make a model of your tooth.
	Rinse your mouth and relax for a while.

○ PULP CAPPING

Dentist	It's a deep cavity. The cavity is close to the nerve.
	But, the nerve doesn't seem to be inflamed.

　　　　　て様子をみようと思います.
次回の治療で
　歯科医　どうですか. 痛みはありましたか？
　患　者　大丈夫です.
　歯科医　よかったですね. これでしばらく様子をみましょう.
　　　　　何かありましたら, またおいでください.

○ **抜髄**
　歯科医　いつから痛くなりましたか？
　患　者　2, 3日前から痛み始めました.
　歯科医　どんなときに痛みますか？
　患　者　初めは噛むと痛かったのですが, しだいにじっとしていても痛くなって, 痛み止めを飲みました.
　歯科医　どんな痛みでしたか？
　患　者　ズキズキと痛みました. 眠れませんでした.
　歯科医　痛み止めは効きましたか？
　患　者　あまり効きませんでした.
　歯科医　あなたの場合は歯の神経を取らないとだめなようです.
　　　　　冠を被せて治療が終わるまで, あと4〜5回治療が必要です.
　　　　　通っていただけますね？

○ **感染根管治療**
　患　者　歯茎が腫れて痛いのです.
　歯科医　腫れたのは, 初めてですか？
　患　者　2度目です.
　歯科医　歯茎に膿の出口がありますね.
　　　　　エックス線検査から判断すると, 根の治療にかなりの回数が必要になるかもしれません. 根の先に黒くなっているところがありますね.
　　　　　ここに膿が溜まっているのですよ.
　　　　　冠を外して, 歯に穴をあけ, 膿を出します.
治療後に
　歯科医　終わりました. 膿を出しましたので, 心配はありません.
　　　　　薬を出します. 化膿止め, 腫れ止めと痛み止めです.

ENDODONTICS & OPERATIVE DENTISTRY

So, let's not take out the nerve, I'll cap the nerve with medicine.

Next appointment

Dentist   How do you feel? Do you feel any pain?

Patient   No, no problem.

Dentist   That's great. See how it goes.
If you want me to check it, come and see me again.

PULP EXTIRPATION/ PULPECTOMY

Dentist   When did the pain start?

Patient   About two or three days ago.

Dentist   When is it most painful?

Patient   At first it was painful when I bit into something.
I gradually felt a constant pain, and took a painkiller.

Dentist   What kind of pain did you feel?

Patient   I had terrible pain. I couldn't sleep.

Dentist   Was the painkiller effective?

Patient   No, not really.

Dentist   In your case, I think I'll have to take out the nerve.
You'll have to return four or five times until I set a crown.
Can you come back for more treatments?

ROOT CANAL TREATMENT

Patient   My gums look swollen, it's painful.

Dentist   Is it the first time?

Patient   No, the second time.

Dentist   There is an opening of pus on the gum.
Several times will be necessary to clean the root canal by looking at the X-ray. There is a black part around the root tip, right?
This part is where it is suppurating.
I'll remove the crown, make an opening in the tooth, and take the pus out.

After treatment

Dentist   I'm finished, and the pus is taken out, so don't worry.
I'll give you some medicine. There's an antibiotic to stop infection, an antiphlogistic to stop inflammation, and a painkiller for the pain.

レッスン3　歯周治療

○歯肉炎

歯科医　今日はどうされましたか．
患　者　右下の歯茎が腫れて，歯磨きのときに出血します．
歯科医　確かに歯茎が赤くなって，少し腫れていますね．歯茎を診せてください．

検査後

歯科医　歯と歯茎の境目の歯肉溝の深さは3mm以下で，エックス線検査では歯を支えている骨は吸収されていませんでした．
　　　　これは，歯肉炎の症状です．
患　者　歯肉炎ってどんな病気ですか．
歯科医　歯の周りについているプラークによって引き起こされる病気で，あなたの場合のように歯茎が赤く腫れたり，歯磨きのときに出血したりするのが典型的な症状です．
患　者　治りますか．
歯科医　プラークや歯石をきれいに落として，お口の中を清潔に保つように心掛けてください．今の段階で治療すれば大丈夫ですよ．
患　者　放っておくとどうなりますか．
歯科医　歯茎の炎症がひどくなって，さらに広がっていくかもしれません．そのために歯茎が下がったり，歯を支えている骨が徐々に吸収したりし始めることがあります．
患　者　それは大変ですね．早速，治療をしてください．
歯科医　わかりました．まずは，プラークをきれいに落とすことが大切です．まず，プラークをわかりやすくするために，赤く染め出してみましょう．

歯垢染色後

歯科医　鏡を見てください．
患　者　口じゅう真っ赤ですね．
歯科医　赤く染まっているところが，磨けていないところです．
患　者　1日3回歯を磨いています．どこか磨き方にわるいところがあるなら教えてください．
歯科医　それでは歯磨きの練習をしてみましょう．鏡を見ながら，いつもの磨き方で赤いところを落としてみてください．
患　者　こんな磨き方でいいですか．
歯科医　歯と歯茎の境目にちょうどよい角度で毛先が当たっていますが，少しブラッシング圧が強いようです．もう少し力を抜いて小刻みに動かしてみてください．

LESSON 3 PERIODONTAL TREATMENT

○ GINGIVITIS

Dentist   What can I do for you today?

Patient   My lower back right gums are swollen, and they bleed when I brush my teeth.

Dentist   I see. Your gums look reddish and are slightly swollen. Let me check your gums.

After the examination

Dentist   The depths of gingival sulcus between teeth and gums are no more than 3 mm and the bone supporting your teeth is not destroyed according to the X-rays. These are the symptoms of gingivitis.

Patient   What kind of disease is gingivitis?

Dentist   It is caused by the dental plaque that is attached to the tooth surface and its typical symptoms are redness and swelling of the gums and bleeding during tooth brushing as seen in your mouth.

Patient   Will it get better?

Dentist   Let's remove the dental plaque and tartar and try to keep your mouth clean. Your gums will be fine if they are treated at this stage.

Patient   What happens if it is left untreated?

Dentist   The inflammation of the gums will increase and may spread eventually. I'm afraid that your gums will begin to recede and that the bone supporting your teeth will gradually begin to be destroyed.

Patient   Oh, that's terrible. Please begin the treatment.

Dentist   OK. First of all, it is important to remove the dental plaque thoroughly. In order to see the dental plaque, I will dye it red.

After dyeing the plaque red

Dentist   Take a look inside your mouth with the mirror.

Patient   My mouth is full of red areas.

Dentist   The red area indicates the dental surface where the toothbrush didn't reach.

Patient   I brush my teeth three times a day. Please tell me if there are any problems with my tooth brushing method.

Dentist   Well, let's practice it. Brush your teeth as usual and remove the red deposit looking at the mirror.

Patient   What do you think of my way of brushing teeth?

Dentist   It's pretty good that you brush the border between teeth and gums at a right angle. However, your brushing force seems to be a little too strong. Grip the toothbrush more gently and move it with short strokes.

◯ 歯周炎

歯科医　今日はどうされましたか．
患　者　最近，左下の奥歯がグラグラするような感じがします．
歯科医　いつ頃から，グラグラし始めましたか．
患　者　2～3か月前からです．
歯科医　食事をするときに痛みはありますか．
患　者　特に痛いわけではありませんが，固い物が噛めません．
歯科医　それでは，歯茎の詳しい検査をして，エックス線検査してみましょう．

検査後

歯科医　奥歯のエックス線写真を見てください．歯を支えている歯槽骨が，2／3程度吸収しています．歯と歯茎の間の歯周ポケットの深さが7mmありました．歯周炎という歯茎の退縮や歯槽骨の吸収を起こす病気にかかったために，歯がぐらぐらと動き出したのです．
患　者　どうすればよいのでしょうか．
歯科医　放っておくと，歯が抜け落ちてしまうかもしれません．これ以上の歯周炎の進行を食い止めることが大切です．まずは，プラークを歯ブラシでできるだけきれいに取り除いてください．
　　　　プラークは，歯周炎の主な原因です．
患　者　わかりました．できるだけきれいに磨きます．
歯科医　歯ブラシを上手に使えるようになったら，歯間ブラシとフロスの練習もしましょう．歯と歯の間をきれいに磨くのに大変役立ちます．それから，歯に付着した歯石を取ったり，咬み合わせを調整したりします．
患　者　ところで歯石って何ですか．
歯科医　歯石は，歯の周りにミネラルが沈着してできた堅い固まりです．
　　　　歯石の表面はザラザラしているので，周りにプラークがつきやすくなり，それが歯茎に炎症を起こします．
患　者　歯石を取るときは，痛いですか．
歯科医　麻酔をしてから取るので，大丈夫ですよ．

スケーリング後

患　者　痛くなかったです．
歯科医　よかったですね．歯石を取った後も，歯磨きを怠るとまたすぐに歯石がつきます．歯石がつくのを予防するためにも口腔内を清潔に保つことが大切です．

○ PERIODONTITIS

Dentist	What can I do for you today?
Patient	My lower back left teeth are feeling loose.
Dentist	When did you realize it?
Patient	It started 2 to 3 months ago.
Dentist	Do you feel pain when you chew on something?
Patient	It's not painful, but I can't bite anything hard.
Dentist	I see. Let me do a thorough examination of your gums. Then, I will take X-rays.

After the examination

Dentist	Look at the X-ray of your teeth. Two thirds of the alveolar bone, which supports your teeth, is destroyed. The depth of the periodontal pocket between the tooth and gum is 7 mm. You are suffering from periodontitis, which causes recession of the gums and loss of alveolar bone. This is why your teeth are loose.
Patient	What should I do?
Dentist	If it is left untreated, your teeth may fall out. It's important to prevent further progress of periodontitis. The first thing you should do is to remove the dental plaque by brushing your teeth as completely as possible. Dental plaque is the main cause of periodontitis.
Patient	I see. I will brush my teeth as completely as possible.
Dentist	After gaining better skill at tooth brushing, I'll show you how to use an interdental brush and dental floss. It's very useful for cleaning between your teeth. Then, I will remove the tartar attached to the teeth and adjust your biting condition.
Patient	By the way, what's tartar?
Dentist	Tartar is a mineralized deposit formed on the tooth surface. The surface of tartar is rough and prone to harbor the dental plaque that causes inflammation in gums.
Patient	Is it painful to remove tartar?
Dentist	I'll give you a local anesthetic. The treatment should be painless.

After scaling

Patient	I didn't feel any pain.
Dentist	That's good. I have removed the tartar, but it will appear again if you don't brush your teeth adequately. To prevent the deposition of tartar, it is important to keep your

○ 急性歯周膿瘍

歯科医　今日はどうされましたか．
患　者　右上奥の歯茎が腫れました．
歯科医　いつ頃から腫れましたか．
患　者　昨日からです．
歯科医　痛みますか．
患　者　一日中，痛みが続いています．
歯科医　お口の中を診てみましょう．右上の奥歯の歯茎が腫れていますね．歯茎に感染が起きているようです．そこを洗浄しましょう．

ポケット洗浄後

歯科医　腫れているところを洗浄しました．
患　者　少し楽になりました．ありがとうございます．
歯科医　咬み合わせも問題がないか調べてみます．
　　　　奥歯でカチカチ嚙んでみてください．
患　者　歯を咬み合わせたときに，鋭い痛みがあります．
歯科医　歯茎が腫れているところの歯が，反対側の歯と強く当たりすぎているようです．咬み合わせの調整をしましょう．
患　者　咬合調整後，嚙んだときも楽になりました．
歯科医　痛み止めと抗生剤を処方しておきます．説明書に従って，服用してください．2～3日で歯茎の腫れは引くと思いますが，また同じ症状が再発するかもしれません．今のうちに，きちんと歯周病の治療をしておきましょう．

mouth clean.

ACUTE PERIODONTAL ABSCESS

Dentist   What can I do for you today?

Patient   My upper back right gums are swollen.

Dentist   When did it start?

Patient   It started yesterday.

Dentist   Does it hurt?

Patient   It aches all day long.

Dentist   Let me take a look inside your mouth. Your upper back right gums are swollen. An infection seems to have accumulated there. I will wash it out.

After pocket irrigation

Dentist   The infection was drained from the swollen part.

Patient   I feel a little better now. Thank you very much.

Dentist   I will examine your bite to see if there are any problems in your biting condition. Tap your back teeth together.

Patient   I have a sharp pain when I do that.

Dentist   The teeth in the swollen gums are hitting the opposing teeth too hard. I'll adjust it.

Patient   After adjustment of biting condition. I feel less pain now.

Dentist   I will prescribe a certain kind of antibiotic and pain-reliever. Please follow the instructions carefully. The swelling of your gums will disappear in a few days, but I'm afraid it might reappear. It's important to get your gums treated completely.

レッスン4　クラウン・ブリッジによる補綴処置

クラウンによる補綴処置
◯初診日
　　歯科医　はじめまして．補綴担当の松中といいます．
　　　　　　今日はどうなさいましたか？
　　患　者　実は昨日，右下の奥歯に詰めてあった物が外れてしまったんです．
　　歯科医　痛みはありますか？
　　患　者　いいえ，ありません．
　　歯科医　では診てみましょう．歯茎は問題ないようですね．
　　　　　　歯を軽くトントンしますよ．もし痛かったら教えてくださいね．
　　患　者　いいえ，痛くありません．
　　歯科医　この歯は昔，神経の治療をされたことはありますか？
　　患　者　はい，学生時代にしました．
　　歯科医　では，レントゲンを撮ってみましょう．
　　　　　　あちらがレントゲン室ですので，移動をお願いします．
エックス線写真を示しながら
　　歯科医　根っこの先に異常はないようです．歯の上のほうだけが欠けたようですね．
　　　　　　でも同じように詰めるだけでは，また外れたり，歯が欠けたりするかもしれませんので，冠を被せたほうがいいと思います．
　　患　者　どんなふうにするんですか？
　　歯科医　はい，まず歯に土台を立てます．そしてそれを削って，型をとって，冠を被せます．
　　　　　　冠の種類がいくつかありますので，どれにするか選んでいただけます．
　　患　者　どんな種類ですか？
　　歯科医　見本をお見せしましょう．金属の冠と，歯の色をしたセラミックスを金属に焼きつけた冠と，全部セラミックスだけでできた冠があります．費用はこの表の通りですが，保険がきくものときかないものがあります．
　　　　　　どの材料にしても，むし歯や歯周病にならないようにしっかり歯磨きすることが大切です．
　　患　者　今決めなければいけませんか？
　　歯科医　いいえ．次回来られるときまでで大丈夫です．

◯支台築造のための形成，印象
　　歯科医　こんにちは，具合はいかがですか？

LESSON 4 PROSTHODONTIC TREATMENTS USING CROWNS & BRIDGES

PROSTHODONTIC TREATMENT USING A CROWN
○ THE FIRST VISIT

Dentist   Hi, nice to meet you, I am a prosthodontist and my name is Matsunaka.
What can I do for you today?

Patient   Well, my filling in the right lower back tooth came out yesterday.

Dentist   Do you feel any pain?

Patient   No, I don't.

Dentist   Shall I check your teeth? The gum around the tooth appears to be good.
I'm going to tap on the tooth. Tell me if you feel any pain.

Patient   Not at all.

Dentist   Have you ever had a root canal treatment in this tooth?

Patient   Yes, in my school days.

Dentist   Let's take an X-ray of the tooth.
The X-ray room is right over there. Please go over there.

In showing the X-ray dental film

Dentist   There is no bad part around the root apex, here. The fracture is limited to the coronal area. But, re-fillings tend to come out, and result in tooth fracture. So, we should make a new crown.

Patient   Could you tell me the procedure?

Dentist   Sure. At first, I'll make a base in the tooth. Next, I'll grind the tooth for crown preparation, take an impression, and fabricate a new crown.
There are several types of crown. You can choose the one you want.

Patient   What types are there?

Dentist   I'll show you some samples. These are metal crowns, tooth colored ceramic-fused-to-metal crowns, and all ceramic crowns. As shown in this price list, a metal crown is covered by insurance, but the others aren't.
Whichever materials you choose, proper tooth brushing is important to avoid cavities and gum disease.

Patient   Do I have to choose the materials now?

Dentist   No, you can tell me during your next appointment.

○ PREPARATION AND IMPRESSION FOR A POST CORE

Dentist   How are you today?

患　者　歯が1本抜けたような感じで，食事がしにくいのですが，でも大丈夫です．あのー，冠は金属に歯の色をつけたものでお願いします．
歯科医　わかりました．では，今日は土台のために，歯を削って型をとりましょう．

印象後
歯科医　今日は仮のふたをしたので，ガムみたいなべたつく物を食べると外れることがありますから，気をつけてくださいね．次回は土台と仮歯をはめる予定です．

患　者　はい，ありがとうございました．

技工室にて
歯科医　築造用の印象です．ファイバーポストとテックをお願いします．
　　　　メタルボンドなので，頬側はショルダーにしてください．

技工士　わかりました．予約は1週間後ですね．

○クラウンのための支台歯形成
歯科医　今日は，歯に土台を立てて，仮歯をつけましょう．
患　者　はい．
歯科医　お口を開けていただけますか？適合ピッタリですね．
　　　　（衛生士に向かって）レジンセメントを練ってください．
衛生士　はい，準備できました．

セメント重合後
歯科医　土台ができました．では，冠が入るように歯を削りますよ．

形成終了後
歯科医　イスを起こします．うがいをどうぞ．

○印象，咬合採得，色調採得
歯科医　それでは次に型をとりましょう．
　　　　（衛生士に向かって）小さいトレーと圧排糸を用意してください．パテ，インジェクションの1回法です．
　　　　どうぞ楽にして鼻で息をしてください．

印象材硬化後
歯科医　型を外しますよ．
　　　　今度は咬み合わせの記録をとります．このシリコンを奥歯で噛んでくださいね．
　　　　はい，お口を開けてください．
　　　　（衛生士に向かって）技工士さんを呼んでください．
衛生士　はーい．

PROSTHODONTIC TREATMENTS USING CROWNS & BRIDGES

Patient   Just fine, except I couldn't chew well. It feels as if my tooth was missing. By the way, I'd prefer a tooth-colored metal crown.

Dentist   OK. Today, I'll drill the tooth and take an impression for the base.

After taking the impression

Dentist   I made a temporary cap today. If you eat sticky food like chewing gum, the temporary cap might come off. So, please be careful. Next time I'll set the base, and temporary crown.

Patient   I see. Thanks.

In the dental laboratory

Dentist   This is an impression for a core build up. Please make a fiber post and a temporary crown. I'm planning to use a porcelain-fused metal crown. So, please shape it into a shoulder type at the buccal cervical margin.

Dental technician   OK. doctor. The next appointment is in a week, isn't it?

◯ TOOTH PREPARATION FOR A CROWN

Dentist   Today, I'll set the base and the temporary crown on the tooth.

Patient   I see.

Dentist   Would you open your mouth? Excellent fit.

(To dental hygienist) Please mix the resin cement.

D.H.   OK. I am ready.

After the cement is polymerized

Dentist   The base is fixed. Next, I'll grind and prepare the tooth for the crown.

After the preparation

Dentist   I'll bring the chair up. Please rinse your mouth.

◯ TAKING IMPRESSIONS, BITE REGISTRATION, AND SHADE

Dentist   OK. Let's take the impression.

(To D.H.) Please prepare a small tray and a retraction cord. I'll apply one-stage technique using putty and injection materials.

Just relax, and breathe through your nose.

After the impression has set

Dentist   I'll take the tray out.

Next, I'll take a bite record. Please bite this silicon with your back teeth together.

Please open your mouth.

(To D.H.) Call the dental technician.

D.H.   OK.

歯科医　（技工士に向かって）シェードはA3に近いけど，歯頸部は褐色のステインがいりますね．
歯科医　（衛生士に向かって）では，テンポラリーハードを練ってください．
　　　　歯を洗いますよ．じゃあ，今日はこれで終わりです．仮歯はあまり強くありませんので，硬い食べ物や粘着性のある食べ物は避けてくださいね．
患　者　はい，どうもありがとうございました．

○受付にて
受　付　次回の予約をおとりいたしましょう．
　　　　製作に1週間ほどかかりますので，次回は7月29日（木）午後3時はいかがですか？
患　者　それでお願いします．
受　付　費用は税込みで9万5,000円になります．
　　　　次回，現金かクレジットカードをご準備いただけますでしょうか？
患　者　はい．
受　付　では，診察券をお返しいたします．お大事にどうぞ．

○クラウンの装着
歯科医　こんにちは．お変わりありませんか？
　　　　これが冠です．では，合わせてみましょう．仮歯を外しますよ．
　　　　当っているところを少し調整しますね．よし，OK.
　　　　今度は高さをチェックしますよ．そっと噛んでみてください．
　　　　いかがですか？
患　者　いいです．
歯科医　色や形はいかがですか？
患　者　本物の歯みたいですね．でも，角が尖っているのがちょっと気になります．
歯科医　そうですか．少し丸めましょう．このくらいはいかがですか？
患　者　よくなりました．
歯科医　では冠をつけましょう．
　　　　（衛生士に向かって）セメントを練ってください．
　　　　これで終りです．イスを起こしますのでうがいをどうぞ．
　　　　できれば，また来月チェックにいらしてください．
患　者　ありがとうございました．
歯科医　どういたしまして．お大事に．

Dentist (To dental technician) I think the shade is close to A3, and the cervical area should be stained with brown.

Dentist (To D.H.) Please mix the Temporary Hard.

I'll spray the tooth. We are all set today. Remember the temporary plastic crown isn't so strong, so don't eat really hard or sticky food.

Patient OK. Thank you very much.

AT THE RECEPTION DESK

Receptionist Would you like to make your next appointment?

It's going to take one week to make your crown, so how about 3:00 P.M., Thursday, July 29th?

Patient That will be fine.

Recept. The total treatment with tax will be ninety-five thousand yen.

Is it OK for you to pay in cash or with credit card at the next appointment?

Patient Of course, sure.

Recept. OK. Here is your appointment card. Please take care.

FIXING THE CROWN

Dentist Good afternoon. How are you?

Here is your crown. Let's try it. I'll remove the temporary crown.

I'll adjust the contact points. OK. Good.

Next, I'll check the height of the crown. Please bite down and gently rub your teeth together. How do you feel?

Patient No problem.

Dentist How about the color and shape?

Patient It really looks like a natural tooth. But, I don't like this sharp corner.

Dentist OK. I'll take the corner off to make it more round. How does that feel now?

Patient Yes, it is fine now.

Dentist I'll set this crown. OK.

(To D.H.) Please mix the cement.

All done. I'll bring the chair up. Please rinse your mouth.

I recommend you to come and get a regular checkup next month.

Patient Thank you very much.

Dentist You're welcome, and take care.

ブリッジによる補綴処置

◯初診日

歯科医　おはようございます．ジョンソンさんですね．澤田と申します．
　　　　今日はどうなさいましたか？
患　者　実は左上の奥歯が1本ないので治してもらいたいんです．
歯科医　いつ頃からないんですか？
患　者　5年くらい前にむし歯で抜かれたんです．
歯科医　そうですか．では診てみましょう．
　　　　治療法は3通りありますが，一つはブリッジで，両側の歯を削る必要があります．二つ目はインプラントで，これは手術が必要です．
　　　　三つ目は取り外しの入れ歯です．
患　者　取り外しや手術はいやだし，歯を削るのもちょっと．
歯科医　それなら歯の一部分だけを削る接着ブリッジというのがありますよ．
患　者　それはいいですね．何回くらいかかりますか？
歯科医　2～3回はかかりますが，その後も定期的にチェックに来られることをお勧めします．

◯ブリッジの装着

歯科医　ジョンソンさんこんにちは．今日はブリッジが完成していますので，合わせてみましょう．
患　者　はい．
歯科医　適合よし．
　　　　今度は高さをチェックします．カチカチ噛んでみてください．
　　　　いかがですか？
患　者　ちょっと高いです．
歯科医　では，調整しましょう．このくらいはいかがですか？
患　者　はい，いいです．
歯科医　今度は，左右に大きく歯ぎしりしてみてください．
　　　　鏡をどうぞ．見た目はどうでしょうか？
　　　　舌触りはいかがですか？
患　者　金属は見えないし，舌触りも大丈夫です．

PROSTHODONTIC TREATMENT USING A FIXED PARTIAL DENTURE (BRIDGE)

○ THE FIRST VISIT

Dentist   Good morning, Mr. Johnson. My name is Sawada.
What can I do for you today?

Patient   Well, I would like to ask you to replace my missing tooth on the left upper back.

Dentist   When did you lose it?

Patient   It was extracted due to a cavity about five years ago.

Dentist   I see. Shall I check your teeth?
We have three treatment options. The first option is a bridge for which we need to grind both teeth adjacent to the space. The second option is an implant that needs a surgical operation. The third option is a removable partial denture.

Patient   I don't want a removable one or surgical treatment. Also, I don't want you to grind my teeth.

Dentist   Well, I recommend a resin-bonded bridge for which we need to trim only one part of your tooth.

Patient   That sounds good. How many times does it take?

Dentist   The treatment needs two or three times at least. After that, you had better come to get regular checkups.

○ FIXING THE BRIDGE

Dentist   Good afternoon, Mr. Johnson. Your bridge is here today.
Let's try it.

Patient   OK. Great.

Dentist   The fit is perfect.
Next, I'll check the height. Please bite together repeatedly.
How does it feel?

Patient   I feel a high spot a little bit.

Dentist   I see. I'll adjust it. How about now?

Patient   Yes, it's fine.

Dentist   Please move your teeth to the left and the right.
Please hold this mirror. What do you think about the appearance?
Does it bother your tongue?

Patient   No metal is seen, and no trouble on the tongue, either.

歯科医　では，接着しましょう．
　　　　（衛生士に向かって）スーパーボンドと赤のエッチング液を用意してください．ブリッジの内面はアルミナでサンドブラスト処理してから，メタルタイトを塗布してください．
衛生士　表面処理できました．
歯科医　しばらくお口を開けたままでお願いします．スプレーで洗いますよ．

ブリッジの装着後

歯科医　はい終りました．イスを起こします．うがいをどうぞ．
　　　　1時間ほど何も食べないようにお願いします．歯磨きのときは歯間ブラシを使ってくださいね．サイズはSがいいと思います．
患　者　持っていますが，なければ買います．ありがとうございました．
歯科医　お大事に．

Dentist	OK. Let's bond it now.
	(To D.H.) Please prepare the Super-Bond and the Red Conditioner.
	Please air-abrade the inside of the bridge with alumina, and prime the surface with the Metaltite primer.
D.H.	The surface treatment is completed.
Dentist	Please keep your mouth open for a while. I'll clean the tooth with spray.

After the bridge is set

Dentist	OK. finished. I'll bring the chair up. Please rinse your mouth.
	Please don't eat anything for one hour. When you clean the bridge, please use an interdental brush. I think the size S will fit.
Patient	I've got one or I'll get one if I don't. Thanks very much.
Dentist	Please take care.

レッスン5　インプラント治療

歯科医　こんにちはアダムスさん．今日はどうされましたか？

患　者　こんにちはバーンズ先生．先月歯周病のためグラグラになっていた右下の奥歯2本を抜歯してもらったのですが，それ以来食事がしづらくて困ってるんです．先生からは取り外し式の義歯を勧められはしましたが，聞くところでは，違和感が強くて，食べ物の味が変わるとか，ときどき義歯が歯茎に食い込んで痛いとかであまり気が進みません．先生，何かほかにいい方法はないものでしょうか？

歯科医　インプラント治療という方法があります．

患　者　あっ，それ聞いたことがあります！それはどんな治療法なんですか？詳しく教えてください．

歯科医　インプラント治療は，手術により顎の骨に金属製のネジを埋め込み，それを支えとして義歯を固定する治療です．人工物の歯の根っこを埋め込んで行う治療法ですので，人工歯根といわれたりもします．通常，歯がなくなった後の治療法とされるブリッジや，取り外し式の義歯と比較して，余計に歯を削る必要がありません．また咬み合わせの力を顎の骨でしっかりと支えることができるので，固定式で噛み応えのいい義歯を使っていただくことができます．

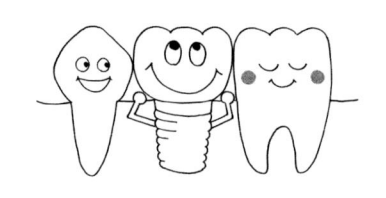

患　者　でも手術が必要なんですよねぇ！？痛そうだなぁ…

歯科医　通常インプラントを埋め込む手術は，それほど大きな手術ではありません．もちろん麻酔をして行いますので痛みもないです．手術の後，噛んだときにちょっと痛むくらいです．

患　者　全身麻酔ですか？

歯科医　いいえ．普通は歯の治療で使う注射の麻酔で行います．
麻酔が効いた後，歯肉を少し切らせていただき，顎の骨にドリルを使ってインプラントを埋め込みます．手術はだいたい1時間程度で終了します．
しかしインプラント治療をするためには，いくつかの検査をしなければなりません．全身的な健康状態からお口の中の咬み合わせや歯周病の状態を把握し，さらにインプラントが入るだけの顎の骨の幅と高さがあるかどうかを，CT検査によって評価します．
それらを総合的に判断して，インプラント治療に向いているかどうか診断します．そして，インプラント治療を行うとすれば，何本のインプラントが必要で，

LESSON 5 IMPLANT THERAPY

Dentist　　Hi, How are you Mr. Adams? How may I help you?

Patient　　Hello, Dr. Barnes. It's been difficult to eat since I lost my right side lower molars last month. (Note* Patient lost her molars due to severe periodontitis). Although, you recommend that I get a removable partial denture, I have heard that it is often uncomfortable. I hear that it may diminish the taste of food and sometimes cause pain at the gum. I don't feel much like wearing the removable denture. Doctor, are there any other solutions?

Dentist　　Recently, we have a method to replace the missing teeth, an implant denture.

Patient　　Oh yes, I have heard of that!
　　　　　Please tell me the details of the implant treatment.

Dentist　　The implant treatment is to fix and support the denture by means of a titanium bolt, which is operatively-inserted into the jaw bone. Namely, the inserted titanium bolt works as an artificial tooth root. Compared to the conventional teeth replacement methods such as the bridge or the removable partial denture, the implant treatment doesn't need any teeth grinding and has a rigid anchor to support the denture.

Patient　　But, this treatment requires surgery, doesn't it? It's a bit scary. It must be painful.

Dentist　　Usually, the implant surgery is not so severe. We of course do it under anesthesia, so you don't feel the pain during the operation. It may be a little bit sore after the operation, as it's healing.

Patient　　Is it performed under general anesthesia?

Dentist　　No, it is usually performed with local anesthesia which we use on usual dental treatments. Under anesthesia, small incisions are made on the gum, then a small hole is prepared in the jawbone and the implant is inserted. The operation is completed in around 1 hour. However, you need to have some other examinations beforehand. At first we check your general health. We examine not only whether you can tolerate the surgery or not but also the risk for the implant treatment. Then, an oral examination in which the condition of occlusion and periodontitis are evaluated. Furthermore, bone volume that can support the implant is investigated by CT scan. Finally, we totally diagnose whether you meet the requirements of implant treatment or not. Then, we

　　　　　　どのような義歯ができるのかという治療計画を立案します．

患　者　インプラント治療ができない場合もあるのですか？
歯科医　はい．まったくできないというケースは稀ですが，大きくないとはいえ手術を行うわけですから，全身的な健康状態によっては注意を要することがあります．特に糖尿病やステロイド使用者など傷の治りや感染のしやすさに影響する持病を持っている方，ほかにも病院に通院中もしくは定期的に投薬を受けている場合はお教えください．病院にかかっていなくても最近健康診断などを受けていない場合は，こちらで血液検査をさせていただくこともあります．また咬み合わせの状態がわるい方，むし歯や歯周病に罹患している方は，インプラントをする前にそれらの治療をしなければなりません．CT 検査でインプラントを埋め込むだけの十分な骨量がないと判断されることもあります．その際はインプラントをしっかり支えるための骨を作るため，骨の量を増やす手術が必要です．
患　者　骨の量を増やす手術ですか？
歯科医　そうです．通常は自分の下顎の奥から骨を採取し，それを移植します．
　　　　　自分の骨ですから問題なく骨の量を増やすことができますが，インプラントをする部分以外に，別に傷をつけなければならないことが大きな欠点です．
　　　　　いずれにしても CT の結果次第になりますので，もしインプラント治療を前向きにお考えでしたら，まず CT 検査を行いましょう．

患　者　お願いします．

アメリカの歯科事情 2　－インプラント治療－

アメリカではインプラント治療は補綴専門医（Prosthodontist）による治療ですが，一般歯科（General Dentist）でもインプラントを行うところが増えています．インプラント埋入はペリオと口腔外科の専門医で行われています．

	make an implant treatment plan including how many implants we need and what type of superstructure is envisioned necessary.
Patient	Are there any risks involved?
Dentist	It is totally rare. However, we do need some special concern about the surgery depending on your general health. Please tell me if you are visiting other hospitals for treatment or taking any over the counter medications. Especially if you are cut or wounded and it's not healing or if you are a compromised patient such as a diabetic, taking steroids or something like that. Even if you don't have any medical problems and have had a regular health checkup recently, we may do a blood test just in case. When you have uncomfortable occlusion, dental caries or periodontitis, you have to treat them before the implant treatment. Sometimes the data of the CT scan reveals that the bone volume would be insufficient for supporting the implant. At that time you additionally require an extra operation for bone augmentation.
Patient	What do you mean an extra operation for bone augmentation!?
Dentist	Well, usually, autogenous bone is harvested from the mandible and grafted on the recipient site. Since the bone is autogenous, bone volume is usually gained without any problem. However, you have to have some extra surgery for the harvesting. That is the big disadvantage. Anyhow, the details of the treatment plan with or without bone grafting and so on, depends on the CT scan results. If you want to go ahead with the implant treatment, the next step is the CT examination. Shall we do the CT examination?
Patient	Yes, please.

レッスン6　可撤性義歯による処置

◯義歯の不適合
　　歯科医　こんにちは．どうしました？
　　患　者　ええ，上の入れ歯の調子がわるいのです．
　　　　　　上の入れ歯が落ちて，うまくしゃべれないのです．
　　歯科医　どれどれ．スミスさん，ほんとうにこの入れ歯はゆるいです．
　　　　　　まず，入れ歯の裏打ちをしましょう．よくなると思います．

義歯のリベースが終わって
　　歯科医　どうですか？
　　患　者　なんか，左のあたりが強い感じがします．
　　歯科医　わかりました．咬合紙で調べます．口を開け
　　　　　　てください．ゆっくり，軽い力でカチカチと
　　　　　　噛んでください．そう，それでいいです．
　　　　　　やはり，左側が強く当たっていました．少し
　　　　　　削ります．お待ちください．いかがですか？
　　患　者　よくなりました．
　　歯科医　また，痛みがでましたら，来てください．

◯義歯の破折
　　歯科医　今日は．どうしました？
　　患　者　入れ歯が割れました．
　　歯科医　どうしたら，割れましたか？
　　患　者　昨夜，煎餅を食べていたら割れました．
　　歯科医　いままで，何回か割れましたか？
　　患　者　はい，この1年で2～3回割れました．
　　歯科医　入れ歯を見せてください．
　　　　　　大丈夫です．40分ぐらい待っていただければ修理できます．
　　　　　　割れた部分が薄いですので，そこに補強線を入れます．
　　　　　　お待ちいただけますか．
　　患　者　はい，大丈夫です．

1時間後，修理が終わって
　　歯科医　大変，お待たせしました．
　　　　　　これから，入れ歯の裏打ちをして，咬み合わせを調整します．
　　患　者　ありがとうございます．

LESSON 6 REMOVABLE PROSTHODONTIC TREATMENT

○ POORLY-FITTING DENTURES

Dentist   Hello. How are you?

Patient   Well, I'm having some problems with my upper denture.

              It keeps falling out. It's really difficult to speak.

Dentist   Let's have a look. Uh-huh. Well, this is very loose.

              First, I'll line your denture for you. That will help.

In finishing the lining of the denture

Dentist   How does it feel?

Patient   It feels a little high on the left side.

Dentist   I see. I'll check it with a biting sheet.

              Open your mouth, please. Please tap your teeth together gently.

              That's good.

              As you said, the left side is a little high. I'll grind it.

              Hang on. How do you feel now?

Patient   Much better.

Dentist   If you feel any pain, please come and see me.

○ BREAKAGE OF DENTURES

Dentist   What can I do for you today?

Patient   My denture broke.

Dentist   Hmm. How did that happen?

Patient   Last night. When I was eating "SENBEI".

Dentist   How many times has it happened?

Patient   Two or three times in the last year.

Dentist   Let's have a look at the denture.

              Don't worry. I can repair this denture in about 40 minutes.

              The broken part is thin, so I'll insert a wire into this part to make it stronger.

              Do you mind waiting?

Patient   No, no problem.

In finishing the repair of the denture after one hour

Dentist   I'm sorry to have kept you waiting so long.

              I'll just line the denture, and adjust the bite. OK?

Patient   Thank you very much.

○ 新しい義歯の製作

診断用模型のための印象

歯科医　入れ歯の調子はいかがですか？
　　　　この先2〜3か月，この入れ歯でやれそうですか？
患　者　いいですよ，大丈夫です．
歯科医　そうしましたら，今回から新しい入れ歯の製作に入ります．
　　　　型を2度とり，咬み合わせを調べ，試適，セットとなります．
　　　　少なくとも5回，2か月の通院が必要です．
　　　　料金ですが，保険内で作りますと約8千円，保険外ですと36万円になります．
　　　　保険内で作る入れ歯ですと，土台がプラスチック製ですので厚くなり，異物感が大きく，あまり丈夫ではありません．
　　　　より高価な入れ歯では，土台が金属製になりますので，薄く頑丈です．
　　　　異物感はプラスチックに比較して，ずいぶん少なくなるでしょう．
　　　　歯の部分はどちらも硬いプラスチックですので同じです．
　　　　どちらにしますか？
患　者　どちらが長く使えますか？
歯科医　プラスチックの入れ歯のほうが，割れたりしやすいでしょうね．
患　者　そうですか．そうしますと，プラスチックの入れ歯は少し異物感が大きい．
　　　　金属の入れ歯は少し高い．
　　　　保険の入れ歯を試してみようかと思います．
歯科医　いいですよ．それでは，最初の型をとりましょう．
　　　　大きく口を開けてください．舌を上にあげて，鼻で呼吸をしてください．
　　　　はい，印象材が固まりました，トレイを取り出します．うまくとれてます．
　　　　口をゆすいでください．

精密な印象

歯科医　歯を少し削ります．いいですか？
　　　　痛くないでしょう，心配はいりません．
　　　　トレーを試適して，周りを合わせて，精密な型をとります．
　　　　変な味がするかもしれません．

咬合採得

歯科医　今日は咬み合わせをとります．
　　　　まず，バネがついた仮の入れ歯の土台を口に入れます．
　　　　いかがですか？痛いところがありますか？
患　者　いいえ．痛いところはありません．
歯科医　高いところがないか，確かめます．

NEW DENTURES

Making a preliminary impression

Dentist   How's the condition of your dentures?

Can you use them for another two or three months?

Patient   They seem to be OK.

Dentist   Well, let's get started on the new dentures.

We have to take impressions twice, check your bite, do a trial, and set them.

You'll need to come back at least five times in the next two months.

The cost is going to be about eight thousand-yen if you are covered by insurance,

and about three hundred and sixty thousand yen if you aren't covered.

If it's covered by insurance the denture base material is plastic, so the denture base is thick. It's a strange feeling, and the denture won't be very tough.

A more expensive denture base is made of metal, so the denture is thin and tough. It doesn't feel as strange as plastic. The artificial teeth are the same hard plastics in both cases. Do you know which one you want?

Patient   Which one lasts the longest?

Dentist   I think the plastic denture is apt to break more easily.

Patient   I see. Well, the plastic feels a little strange.

The metal is more expensive, right?

I guess I'll try the plastic one covered by insurance.

Dentist   OK. Well I'll take the first impression.

Please open your mouth. Raise your tongue and breathe through your nose.

OK. It looks ready, I'll remove the tray. Perfect.

Go ahead and rinse your mouth.

Making a final impression

Dentist   Today, I'll grind your teeth a little. Ready?

You probably won't feel any pain. Don't worry.

I'll try this tray in your mouth and adjust it. I'll take a final impression.

You may feel it has a strange taste.

Taking the bite registration

Dentist   Let's take your bite.

First, I'll try the temporary denture base in your mouth.

How does it feel? Does it hurt?

Patient   No, I don't feel any pain.

Dentist   Let's see if you have any high spots.

歯科医は咬合紙でクラスプの当たりを確かめる
　　歯科医　すこし当たっているところがありますので削ります．
　　患　者　私の歯を削るのですか？
　　歯科医　いいえ，バネを削りますから，心配はいりません．
　　　　　　大丈夫です．終わりました．

歯科医は咬合堤を基礎床につけて，咬合堤を軟化する
　　歯科医　リラックスして，ゆっくり噛んでください．
　　　　　　はい，いいです．とてもよかったです．

前歯の試適
　　歯科医　いまから，入れ歯の試適をします．
　　　　　　鏡を見てください．いかがですか？前歯はどうですか？
　　患　者　はい，長すぎるような気がします．
　　歯科医　わかりました．修正しました．今度はどうでしょう？
　　患　者　とても，よくなりました．
　　歯科医　歯の大きさや色はどうでしょうか？
　　患　者　歯が少し大きい感じがあります．
　　　　　　色ももう少し白くしてください．
　　歯科医　わかりました．歯の大きさを小さくして，色を白くしましょう．
　　　　　　2週間後に義歯はできあがります．

義歯の装着
　　歯科医　新しい入れ歯ができあがりました．さっそく入れてみます．
　　　　　　いま，痛いところはありますか？
　　患　者　いいえ，ありません．
　　歯科医　それでは，咬み合わせを調べます．
　　　　　　ゆっくりカチカチと噛んでください．
　　　　　　いかがですか？　強く当たっているところはないですか？
　　患　者　左側が強く当たっているような気がします．
　　歯科医　そうですね．たしかに左側が強いですね．少し削りましょう．
　　　　　　これでどうですか？
　　患　者　よくなりました．
　　歯科医　これから入れ歯と歯肉との適合状態をみます．
　　　　　　部分的に強く当たっているところがありましたので，削ります．
　　患　者　よくなりました．いいです．

The dentist checks for high spots on the clasp using an occlusal sheet

Dentist   I'll grind the high spots a little.

Patient   Are you going to grind my teeth?

Dentist   No, just the clasp, don't worry.

    All right. I've finished.

The dentist puts a wax occlusion rim on the base plate, and softens the wax rim

Dentist   Please relax, bite on the wax slowly.

    That's good, great.

Trial of the anterior teeth

Dentist   Well, let's try the wax denture.

    Have a look in the mirror. What do you think? Are the front teeth OK?

Patient   Hmm. The front teeth look too long.

Dentist   I see, I'll adjust that. How do you feel now?

Patient   That's better. Great.

Dentist   What do you think about the color and size?

Patient   I wonder if the teeth are a little too big.

    And I'd like to have whiter teeth.

Dentist   I see, I'll change the size to a smaller one, and the color, OK.

    The new dentures will be completed in 2 weeks next.

Set the new denture

Dentist   Here are the new dentures. Now, let's try them.

    How do they feel? Do they hurt anywhere?

Patient   No, not now.

Dentist   Well, I'll check the bite.

    Please tap your teeth together slowly.

    How do you feel? Do you feel any high spots?

Patient   I feel a high spot on the left side.

Dentist   I see, uh huh. The part on the left side is certainly high. Yes, it looks high. I got it.

    I'll grind this part down a little. How does it feel now?

Patient   Much better.

Dentist   Well, I'll check the fit of the dentures.

    There are several areas of heavy contact. I'll grind these.

Patient   They feel good. Great.

レッスン7　歯科予防処置（ケア）

○口臭予防

患　者　友達から口臭がするって言われたのですが．

歯科医　そうですか．口臭の原因の大半はお口の中にあります．
　　　　歯周病や大きなむし歯，歯や舌の汚れが原因となりますので，まずそのチェックが必要ですね．

患　者　よろしくお願いします．

ケース1　60代男性

歯科医　このブリッジの一部分が外れかかって浮いたような状態になっています．ほかの歯とつながっているので取れはしないのですが，外れた金冠の内部のむし歯が進行しているようです．ひどい場合は外してみると中がドロドロになっていることもあります．

患　者　そういえば，最近噛んだときに具合がわるく，気になっていました．

歯科医　とりあえずレントゲンを撮りましょう．

ケース2　40代女性

歯科医　歯周ポケットが4mmを超えて深くなっている歯がたくさんあります．歯周ポケットが深いと中で嫌気性菌が繁殖し，タンパク質を分解してイオウを含んだガスを発生します．
　　　　これが典型的な口臭の原因となります．

患　者　歯周病なんですか？

歯科医　そのようです．ただ，まだそれほど進行してないようです．適切なブラッシングと歯石除去でほぼよくなると思いますよ．

患　者　よくなったら口臭もなくなりますか？

歯科医　ほかに原因がなければ口臭もなくなると思います．いずれにしても歯を守るためには歯周基本治療が必要ですね．

ケース3　30代女性

歯科医　むし歯も歯周病もないようですが，プラークがたくさん溜まっています．あと舌苔といって，舌の表面が汚れていて菌が増えているようです．

患　者　どうすればいいですか？

歯科医　ブラッシングと舌の清掃の指導をしたいと思いますが，歯の汚れを染め出ししてもいいですか？
　　　　口元が少し赤くなります．

患　者　これから仕事なんです．お店で働いているのでちょっと困ります．

歯科医　では今日は染め出しをせずに，指導しましょう．この次は染め出しをしたいの

LESSON 7 PREVENTIVE DENTISTRY

○ PREVENTION OF HALITOSIS

Patient　One of my friends said I had a bad breath.

Dentist　All right. Mainly, the causes of malodor exist in the mouth.
　　　　　Because of periodontal disease, a big cavity, a dirty tongue and dirty teeth; therefore, it is necessary to check them first.

Patient　OK. Can we do that today?

Case 1, male 60's

Dentist　A part of this bridge is detaching and is in a floating condition. Since it is connected to the other teeth, it will not come out, but dental caries in the detaching crown will probably get worse. In severe cases, when you remove the bridge, the abutment teeth are completely rotten.

Patient　Well, recently my teeth don't feel right.

Dentist　Let's take an X-ray.

Case 2, female 40's

Dentist　Many of your teeth have deep periodontal pockets exceeding a depth over 4mm. When periodontal pockets become deep, anaerobes begin to grow inside pockets. They decompose protein and produce several gasses containing sulfide. This is a typical cause of the bad smell.

Patient　Do I have periodontal disease?

Dentist　Yes, you do. However, your case is not so severe. Your condition will be better soon after learning appropriate tooth brushing and removing tartar.

Patient　When my gum condition improves, does my halitosis improve?

Dentist　Yes. If you do not have any other causes of halitosis, it will improve. Anyway, basic periodontal treatment will be needed to protect your teeth.

Case 3, female 30's

Dentist　You have no dental caries or periodontal disease, but dental plaque is accumulating on your teeth. In addition, the surface of your tongue is a little dirty from the increasing bacteria, which is called tongue plaque.

Patient　What should I do?

Dentist　I would like to show you how to brush your teeth and clean your tongue properly. May I show you where the dental plaque is on your teeth with this disclosing agent? The edges of your mouth will become a little reddish.

Patient　No, I don't want to do it since I will have to work at a shop after this.

Dentist　Yes, I understand. This time I'll instruct you without the disclosing agent. However

で，染め出しのできる日に来てください．

患　者　わかりました．よろしくお願いします．

ケース4　40代女性
歯科医　むし歯も歯周病もなく，歯磨きもきれいにできているようです．舌の汚れもありません．

患　者　口臭がしませんか？

歯科医　マスクを少しずらして診察しましたが，ほとんど気にならない程度です．

患　者　安心しました．でも，また言われるのではないか心配です．

歯科医　客観的に調べるには口臭検査が必要です．次回の来院時にまだ心配なようでしたら紹介状を書きましょう．

○フッ化物による予防処置
ケース1　子供
母　親　この子は甘い物が大好きなのでむし歯にならないか心配です．何かいい予防法はないでしょうか．

衛生士　甘いお菓子やジュースの回数を減らすことが重要です．普通のお菓子をキシリトールガムに代えるだけでもとても効果的です．

母　親　キシリトールガムは与えていますが，ほかのお菓子もよく食べています．

衛生士　そうですか，甘い物がやめられないならフッ化物の応用をお勧めします．

母　親　フッ化物塗布なら何度か受けたことがありますが．

衛生士　フッ化物塗布は年に数回，定期的に受ける必要があります．1〜2回塗布しただけではあまり予防効果はありません．

母　親　3回くらいは受けたので，もう受けなくていいかと思っていました．

衛生士　最後に受けたのはいつですか？

母　親　確か2年くらい前です．

衛生士　ではまた受けたほうがいいと思います．

母　親　わかりました．ほかにも予防する方法があればさせたいのですが？

衛生士　フッ化物洗口があります．当院でも洗口用のフッ化物を処方していますよ．週に1回家庭でうがいするだけです．

母　親　飲み込んだりしても大丈夫なんですか？

衛生士　1〜2回飲み込んだとしても問題ありませんが，うがいはちゃんとできますよね？

	next time I want to demonstrate it using disclosing agent, so please visit me when you can do it.
Patient	Sure. Thank you very much.

Case 4, female 40's

Dentist	You do not have any dental caries or periodontal diseases. Your oral hygiene is good. Your tongue is also clean.
Patient	Do you feel I have bad breath?
Dentist	I slipped my mask off to check, but I didn't smell any bad odor at all.
Patient	I am relieved. But I worry about having bad breath because it's embarrassing.
Dentist	I recommend you get an objective diagnosis by using a machine that detects the levels of bad breath. Next time, if you are still worried about it, I will write a reference letter.

C FLUORIDE APPLICATION

Case 1, child

Mother	My son likes sweets very much, therefore, I worry about whether my son will develop dental caries. Would you show me some good preventive methods?
D.H.	Reducing the number of times he eats sweets and drinks sweet beverages is very important. Exchanging sweets for xylitol gum is also very effective to prevent dental caries.
Mother	I sometimes give him xylitol gum, but he eats other sweets very often.
D.H.	All right. When it is difficult to control the habits of eating sweets, fluoride application is recommended.
Mother	Topical fluoride application was conducted on him several times before.
D.H.	In case of topical fluoride applications, several and continuous applications are necessary throughout the years. One or two applications can not prevent dental caries.
Mother	I didn't think it was necessary anymore, as he has already had it three times.
D.H.	When was the last time?
Mother	Maybe, two years ago.
D.H.	Then, I recommend you to do it again.
Mother	Yes, I understand. Are there any other preventive methods to try out?
D.H.	Rinsing his mouth with fluoride is also effective. We can prescribe fluoride mouth rinse. He just needs to rinse only once a week at home.
Mother	What if my son swallows it?
D.H.	Swallowing the fluoride solution once or twice will not affect him. Make sure he rinses well.

母親　はい．

衛生士　ではちゃんと吐き出すように見守ってあげてください．あまりおいしくはないので普通は飲み込みませんよ．

ケース2　20代女性

患　者　歯はよく磨いているつもりなのですが，子どもの頃からむし歯になりやすくて困っています．何かいい方法はありませんか．

歯科医　歯磨きは基本ですが，フッ化物の利用がとても効果的です．

患　者　どうすればいいのでしょうか？

歯科医　家庭ではフッ化物配合歯磨剤や洗口剤の使用が効果的です．歯科医院や保健所ではフッ化物塗布を受けることができます．

患　者　歯磨きは1日2回しています．確か「フッ化物」って書いてあったと思います．

歯科医　一番手軽な方法がそれです．日本では1,000ppmのフッ化物が入ったものが売られています．買うときには必ず確認してくださいね．それから，フッ化物入りの歯磨剤を使ったときは吐き出した後に，軽く一度だけ水ですすぐようにしてください．口の中のフッ化物濃度を高い状態に保つことによって効果が持続します．

患　者　でも，1回だけだと味が残って気持ちわるくないですか？

歯科医　慣れれば何ともありませんよ．市販の洗口剤などのほうがよほど刺激が強いんです．出かける前や職場での昼食後などは，歯磨剤の香りが残るのでいいと思います．

患　者　へえ，試してみます．ほかに予防法はありますか．

歯科医　もっと徹底的に予防するには，フッ化物洗口とフッ化物塗布があります．私費になりますが当院でも行っていますので，こちらのパンフレットをご覧ください．

◯ブラッシング指導

ケース．30代男性

衛生士　こちらの手鏡を持って見てください．色素で染まっているところが磨き残しの部位です．

患　者　磨いてきたのに結構残っているものですね．

衛生士　そうですね．きれいに磨くのはむずかしいんですよ．1日に何回磨いてますか？

患　者　2回は磨いてます．

衛生士　何分くらい磨きますか？

Mother	Yes, I'll make sure he does.
D.H.	Good. Please supervise him. But children usually do not swallow it as the taste is not so good.

Case 2, female 20's

Patient	Although I brush my teeth very often, I am having trouble as I've been prone to dental caries since childhood. Do you have any good preventive methods?
Dentist	Basically tooth brushing is important. However, application of fluoride is more effective.
Patient	Great! How do I do it?
Dentist	The use of toothpaste containing fluoride and mouth rinse are very effective at home. Dental clinics or health centers also provide topical fluoride application.
Patient	I brush my teeth at least twice a day. Now that you mention it, I saw the word "fluoride" written on the toothpaste.
Dentist	That is the easiest way. In Japan, toothpaste containing 1,000 ppm of fluoride is available everywhere. Be sure to check that the toothpaste contains it when you buy it. When you use toothpaste containing fluoride, only rinse your mouth once after you spit it out. The preventive effect continues by maintaining high fluoride concentration in your mouth.
Patient	Only once? It is OK if the taste remains?
Dentist	It's no problem. The taste is pleasant when you get used to do it. Regular mouth rinsing agents on the market are more irritating. I think the good smell of toothpaste is preferable when you are going out or at the workplace after lunch.
Patient	Yes, I will try it. Do you recommend any other methods?
Dentist	To prevent dental caries more completely I recommend fluoride mouth rinsing and topical fluoride application. It is not covered by insurance and we can do it in this clinic. Please read this leaflet.

C INSTRUCTIONS FOR TOOTHBRUSHING

Case, male 30's

D.H.	Look at your teeth with this mirror. The red area colored by disclosing agent is the dental plaque you couldn't remove by brushing.
Patient	Wow. There's a lot even though I brushed my teeth before I came here.
D.H.	I know. It's difficult to brush effectively. How many times do you brush your teeth a day.
Patient	At least, twice a day.
D.H.	For how long?

患　者　　計ったことありませんが，1〜2分じゃないでしょうか？
衛生士　　回数は2回でもいいのですが，いつも短時間だとどうしても磨き残しの部位がでてきます．誰にでも癖があるので，磨きにくい場所はどうしても残ることが多いですね．たとえば，この青く染まっているところは何日もプラークが残って成熟したところです．
患　者　　成熟ってどういうことですか？
衛生士　　プラークは食べかすではなく細菌の塊です．それが何日も経って成熟してくると細菌の種類が変わってきます．そしてバイオフィルムを形成し簡単には取れにくくなっていくのです．その状態がむし歯や歯周病の原因になっていきます．
患　者　　怖いですね．どうすればいいんでしょうか？
衛生士　　1日に1度は時間をかけてていねいに磨くのが基本です．

患　者　　何分くらい磨けばいいのでしょうか？
衛生士　　人にもよりますが，プラークを完全に除去しようとすると10〜15分くらいはかかります．時間がもったいないので，テレビを見ながらとか，何かをしながら磨くといいですよ．「ながらブラッシング」と呼んでいます．
患　者　　歯磨剤は使うのですか？
衛生士　　「ながらブラッシング」では使いません．唾液も溜めないで自然と飲み込むようにしてください．
　　　　　雑談しながら磨くと自然にできますよ．
患　者　　わかりました．今日から早速やってみます．フロスはどうですか？
衛生士　　フロスも大変効果的ですが，今日はまずブラッシング法を指導しましょう．ブラッシングが上手にできるようになったらフロスのやり方を教えますね．

患　者　　わかりました．
衛生士　　では，ペンを持つように軽く持って，肘をおろして，染まっているところを磨いてみてください．軽く横に小さく動かします．
患　者　　こうですか？
衛生士　　もっと力を抜いてください．軽く歯の表面を滑るような感じで磨くといいです．上の奥歯を磨くときは口を小さくして，頰を横に引っ張るようにして磨いてください．一番奥の歯がとても大切です．ここは磨きにくいので時間をかけて磨いてください．
患　者　　どういう順番で磨いたらいいですか？
衛生士　　奥歯の磨きにくい部位から始めて，2本ずつ，ずらしながら順番に磨いていくとあまり磨き残しがありません．
　　　　　歯の裏側も忘れないように．

Patient	I never check the time, but maybe one or two minutes I think.
D.H.	Twice a day is OK, but if it isn't done long enough or effectively, dental plaque will not be removed in some areas. There are some areas in particular that are difficult to reach. For example, this blue colored area shows us the matured dental plaque which has not been removed for several days.
Patient	What is "matured"?
D.H.	Dental plaque that is not food debris, but a cluster of oral bacteria. When it matures after several days, the kinds of bacteria change gradually, and form a biofilm, which is difficult to remove. This condition leads to dental caries and periodontal diseases.
Patient	Oh, scary. What should I do.
D.H.	It is essential to brush your teeth long enough once a day to get rid of the dental plaque.
Patient	How long should I brush my teeth?
D.H.	Although it depends on the person, it takes 10 to 15 minutes to remove dental plaque completely. Since it is time consuming, I recommend you to do it while watching television, or doing something else. We call it "Nagara brushing".
Patient	How about toothpaste?
D.H.	You don't have to use toothpaste while "Nagara brushing". Also, don't pool your saliva in your mouth, instead swallow it gradually. You can do it while talking to someone in a natural manner.
Patient	Yes I understand. I will give it a try. How about flossing?
D.H.	Dental flossing is very effective, however, I want to focus on tooth brushing today. When you get used to brushing thoroughly and effectively, I will teach you dental flossing.
Patient	Yes, I understand.
D.H.	Yes, please grip the tooth brush lightly like holding a pencil. Then, lower your elbow and brush the colored area. Move it horizontally with short strokes.
Patient	This way?
D.H.	Release your grip more and relax. Brush lightly, like the brush is sweeping on the teeth. When you brush upper molars, close your mouth a little and stretch your cheek toward the side with the tooth brush. The back molars are the most important. Take a long time as it is difficult to brush there.
Patient	In which order should I brush my teeth?
D.H.	Start from the difficult part, the back molars, sliding gradually two teeth at a time. This method reduces the chance of missing the dental plaque. Don't forget to brush the backside of the teeth.

患　者　こんなに部位を意識して磨いたことはありませんでした．
衛生士　磨きやすいところばかり磨いても効果ありませんからね．
患　者　電動歯ブラシや音波ブラシはどうですか？
衛生士　最近の音波ブラシはとてもよくできています．ただ，いくらよい音波ブラシでも毛先が歯面にきちんと当たっていないとプラークはとれません．それから非常に高速で動くので，手用歯ブラシと違って磨き過ぎに注意してください．磨き過ぎると歯茎が下がることがあります．ですから２〜３分で一時停止したりするものが多いようです．
患　者　そうですか．
衛生士　１日１回程度，上下それぞれ２〜３分ずつ磨けば十分です．短くても手で磨くのと同じように，少しずつずらしながらすべての歯面をまんべんなく磨いてください．歯と歯茎の境目を狙って当てるだけでいいので，簡単で効率よくプラーク除去ができます．

アメリカの歯科事情３　−歯科検診と予防−

アメリカで主治医によって行われる歯科検診では，初診の際にエックス線写真撮影，歯石を取る作業，歯磨きおよびフロッシングの指導，むし歯予防のためのフッ化物塗布をします．もし治療の必要がなければ，また半年後の予約をします．半年ごとの検診の主な理由は，むし歯の早期発見，フッ化物によるむし歯予防，そして歯石除去による歯肉炎また歯周病の予防などがあげられます．アメリカでは多くの州でむし歯予防に効果がある水道水へのフッ化物添加（フロリデーション）が行われています．日本に比べ歯科の治療費が高いこともあってアメリカ国民の予防意識は非常に高く，歯科の知識（デンタルIQ）も高めです．

Patient	I never used to be conscious in this way while tooth brushing.
D.H.	It is not effective to brush only the easy parts.
Patient	How about an electric or sonic tooth brush?
D.H.	Recently sonic tooth brushs are very good. However, even though the apparatus is very nice, it cannot remove dental plaque if the brush tips do not touch the teeth surface adequately. Since it moves with very high speed unlike normal hand toothbrush, you need to prevent over brushing. Over brushing sometimes leads to gum recessions. Many of them are set to temporarily stop within 2 or 3 minutes.
Patient	I didn't know that.
D.H.	It is enough to use it once a day, 2 or 3 minutes each on the upper and lower arch. Although the time is short, gradually move over the whole teeth surfaces, like the method for hand tooth brushing. Just by touching the area between teeth and gum, you can remove dental plaque very easily and effectively.

レッスン8　小児への処置

○ はじめまして
　歯科医　はじめまして．歯医者さんの日高です．
　　　　　お名前教えてくれるかな？
　患　児　（不安そうに）ハナです．
　歯科医　こんにちは，ハナ．ハナは何歳ですか？
　患　児　7歳です．
　歯科医　7歳なんだね，わかりました．ところでハナ，今日はどうしたのかな？
　保護者　むし歯があるようで，左下の歯を痛がっていました．しかし本人が歯医者さんに行きたがりませんでした．
　患　児　だって怖いもん！
　歯科医　その気持ちよくわかるよ，ハナ．だけどむし歯は治さなくちゃね．むし歯は歯医者さんでないと治せない．
　　　　　もう7歳のハナならわかるでしょ？
　患　児　う，うん．
　歯科医　よし，いい子だ．ではまず，お口の中を先生に診せてほしいんだ．この「歯医者さんのミラー」でチェックするよ．イスを倒していいかい？
　患　児　（不安そうに）うん．
　歯科医　よし，ハナはとてもいい子だね．ではイスを倒すよ．

○ 口腔内診査
　歯科医　お口を開けてもらえるかなあ？　おっと，上手に開けてくれてありがとう．よく見えるよ．ご協力ありがとう．
　患　児　う，うん．
　歯科医　左下の奥歯（乳歯）に大きなむし歯があるね．神経に届いているかもしれない．だから痛かったんだね．左下以外にもむし歯があるみたいだよ．まずエックス線写真を撮影してみようか．
　患　児　何それ？痛くない？
　歯科医　もちろん痛くないよ．小さなフィルムを口に入れて，写真を撮るみたいに「はいチーズ」で終わりだよ．頑張れるね．
　患　児　それだったら大丈夫かな．
　歯科医　いい子だね．ではレントゲンを撮りに行こう．

○ 局所麻酔
　歯科医　やっぱり左下はむし歯が神経まで進んでいるね．早急な処置が必要です．その

LESSON 8 TREATMENT FOR A CHILD

◯ THE FIRST VISIT

Dentist　Hi, it's very nice to meet you. I am Dr Hidaka, your dentist. Can you tell me your name?

Patient　(with anxiety) My name is Hana.

Dentist　Hello, Hana. Okay, so how old are you, Hana?

Patient　I'm seven years old.

Dentist　Good. You're seven, I see. So what's going on with your teeth?

Parent　She has a cavity on her lower left-hand side tooth. She complained that it hurts. But she did not allow me to take her to the dentist.

Patient　Because it hurts!

Dentist　Oh yes, I can understand what you are saying. But see, Hana. We have to fix your dental cavity. Only dentists can do that. I believe you are old enough to understand what I am saying. You're already seven years old, right?

Patient　Ye...yes.

Dentist　Good. Then, first I would like you to show me the inside of your mouth. I'll check your teeth with this dental mirror. Can I move your chair to the flat position?

Patient　(with anxiety) Yes...

Dentist　Good. What a good girl you are! Then I will move your chair.

◯ ORAL EXAMINATION

Dentist　Can you open your mouth for me? Oh, thank you very much for showing me your teeth. I can see them very well. I appreciate your helpfulness.

Patient　You... you are welcome.

Dentist　You have a big cavity on your lower left-hand side primary molar. It may have reached the dental pulp. It may cause pain. Also you have more decayed teeth on the other parts. Let's take an X-ray, first.

Patient　What's that? Will it hurt?

Dentist　Of course not. I'm just going to put a small film inside your mouth, and just "say cheese" with me like taking a picture. That'll be it. I believe you can do it. Right?

Patient　Then I can do that.

Dentist　Good girl. Now, let's go to take the X-ray.

◯ PAIN-KILLER SHOT

Dentist　Well, now I can conclude that your big cavity has reached the dental pulp already.

　　　　　ほかにもむし歯があるから，順番に治していこう．
　　　　　1週間に1度程度のペースでしばらく通院してもらうことになるけど，いいかい？
保護者　よろしくお願いします．
患　児　（不満足そうに）うん．
歯科医　ありがとう．先生も頑張るから一緒にむし歯を治そう．ハナならできるはずだよ．だけどね，治療のときには毎回，お薬で歯を眠らせる必要がある．わかるかい？
患　児　うん．
歯科医　よし．やっぱり左下が第一なのは変わりないけど，今日は削って白い材料で埋めるだけの処置ですむ右下から取りかかってみよう．
　　　　　歯を眠らせるお薬のことを「麻酔」というのだよ．これで先生がハナの歯を眠らせる．
　　　　　最初だけチクッとするけど，我慢できるね．
患　児　え！痛いの？痛いのはイヤだ！
歯科医　その気持ちもよくわかるけど，その後は歯が眠ってしまうからまったく痛くないよ．約束する．今まで頑張れたじゃない．そんなハナなら我慢できるはずだよ．そうでしょ？
患　児　う，うん．
歯科医　よし，ハナは本当にいい子だね．先生が10まで数えるから，一緒に数えよう．その間に歯を眠らせるよ．1，2…
患　児　痛い！
歯科医　大丈夫だ．動かないでね．3，4，5，6，7，ハナは7歳だったね，8，9，そして10！ほらできた，できたよ！ハナはなんて強い子なんだ．よく頑張ったね．お口をゆすいでごらん．
患　児　なんかほっぺたが変な感じ．やだ，ふくれて風船みたい．
歯科医　大丈夫，眠らせたからそう感じるだけだよ．
　　　　　鏡を見てごらん．これでもう何も感じないよ．ほらどうだい？
患　児　ほんとだ，何も感じない．
歯科医　では，むし歯退治の治療を始めてもいいかい．
患　児　うん．

◯治療に取りかかる

歯科医　歯を眠らせた後は，まず「ラバーダム」をするよ．

	We need an immediate root canal treatment for it. And since you have more decayed teeth, why don't we get ready for a dental treatment for them one by one? That means you have to visit me around once a week for a while. Is it okay for you?
Parent	Yes, it's okay. Thank you, doctor.
Patient	(Unsatisfyingly) Yes...
Dentist	All right, thank you very much. I'll do my best, so please do your best on your treatment for me. I believe you can handle it. However, we need to make your teeth fall asleep by a drug every time before I begin to fix them. Can you understand me?
Patient	Yes.
Dentist	Good. Actually we have to address lower left-hand side molar first, but why don't we begin at your lower right-hand side, because it requires me just to remove the decay and to fill it with white material.
	We call the drug "a painkiller", which allows me to make your teeth go to sleep. It hurts just a little bit at first, but of course you are brave enough to stand it.
Patient	It hurts? No! I don't like it if it hurts me!
Dentist	I can understand you, Hana. But I promise, you won't feel anything after the shot. I promise. You've been so brave already.
	You are brave enough to stand it, right?
Patient	Ye...Yes.
Dentist	Good. You are really a great girl, Hana. Let's count together to ten. The teeth will fall asleep while we are counting. One, Two...
Patient	Oh, it hurts!
Dentist	You will be all right. Please don't move. Three, Four, Five, Six, Seven, oh it's your age, Eight, Nine, and finally it's Ten! That's it. You made it! You are such a brave girl. You did a great job! Now, you can rinse your mouth, Hana.
Patient	Oh, my cheek feels funny… Yuck! It's like a balloon.
Dentist	Don't worry, because it's sleeping.
	Take your mirror and see it. Now you won't feel anything when I take out the cavity. Look, how do you feel?
Patient	Yeah, I feel nothing.
Dentist	All right.
	May I begin to fix your teeth?
Patient	Yes.

◯ FIXING THE TEETH

Dentist	After the pain-killer, I'll put the "rubber dam" on your mouth.

患　児	ラバーダム？
歯科医	ほら，これがラバーダムだよ．これでむし歯を捕まえて治療しやすくするんだ．こんな感じで．鏡で見てごらん，歯がよく見えるでしょ？
患　児	うん，と頷く(うなず)（ラバーダムをしているため患児はしゃべれない）．
歯科医	では，このタービンでわるいところを取るよ．取ったむし歯はこの掃除機で吸い取らないといけない．ちょっと大きな音がするけど，びっくりしないでね．これが歯医者さんの武器なんだ．動いちゃだめだよ．

歯科医はハイスピードタービンを使い，う蝕を除去する

歯科医	よし，むし歯はみんなどこかへ行ったよ．ハナが頑張ってくれたおかげで先生も頑張れたよ．

歯科医はコンポジットレジンを充塡する

歯科医	削ったところは埋めないとね．いまからプラスチックで埋めるよ．そして表面を磨くんだ． ほら，できた！さあ，ラバーダムを外そう．
患　児	ああ，大変だった．
歯科医	でもハナは上手にできたよ．さあ，もう一度お口を開けて．
患　児	まだ終わってないの？
歯科医	咬み合わせをチェックするんだ．よし，いいみたいだ．終わりだよ．
患　児	これで最後？
歯科医	そうだ，ハナ．本当によくできたよ．お父さん／お母さんも見ていたよ．
保護者	ハナ，本当によく頑張ったね．
患　児	うん！
歯科医	これでハナはどんな歯医者さんの治療もできるようになったはずだよ．次からはいよいよ左下の治療に取りかかるよ．できるかい？
患　児	うん，できるよ！
歯科医	そうだ，その調子だ．約束しよう．
患　児	約束する！

C 保護者への説明

歯科医	今日はハナにリドカインで局所麻酔をしました．唇や頰にしびれを感じているでしょう．
保護者	わかります．
歯科医	1時間程度麻酔が続くでしょう．痛みを感じませんから，子どもは唇や頰を咬んでしまうことがあります．十分に気をつけてあげてください．咬まないよう

Patient	Rubber dam?
Dentist	I'll show you. This is the rubber dam. It holds the dental cavity and makes it easier to fix it. It's like this. Watch this with your mirror. Now you can see your teeth very clearly.
Patient	Yes. (She gives a nod since she cannot speak because of the rubber dam.)
Dentist	Now I am going to take out the bad part with my high-speed handpiece. Then I have to suck them with my vacuum cleaner, too. Please don't be surprised when they make a slight noise. These are my weapons. Please don't move.

Dentist uses the high-speed handpiece and takes out the decayed part.

Dentist	Good, it's all gone now. I could do it because you were great.

Dentist put the composite resin on the teeth.

Dentist	Then we have to fill the space where I removed the decay, the bad part. From now on, I will put the plastic on your teeth. After that, I will polish it up. You made it again! Okay Hana, I'll take off the rubber dam.
Patient	Oh, that was tough.
Dentist	But you did a great job. Just open your mouth again for me.
Patient	It's not finished yet?
Dentist	Not yet, Hana. I'll check your bite. Now, looks okay. It's done.
Patient	That's the last one?
Dentist	Sure. You really did a great job. Your father/ mother was watching you.
Parent	You were really great, sweetie.
Patient	Yes!
Dentist	Hana, I believe now you can handle any dental treatment with me. You can do anything. We will make big progress on your lower left-hand side next time. Tell me that you can do it.
Patient	Yes, I can!
Dentist	That's right! Sounds good. Give me your promise.
Patient	I promise!

C EXPLANATION TO THE PARENT

Dentist	Today I gave her a pain-killer shot. That's a local anesthetics, Lidocaine. Her lip and cheek should be numb.
Patient	I understand.
Dentist	It should last for an hour or so. Children might bite their lip or cheek because they don't feel any pain. Please watch her carefully. And do not let her eat anything for an

	に，麻酔が切れるまでは物を食べさせないでください．
保護者	わかりました．気をつけます．
歯科医	ハナ，君の歯や唇は2時まで眠っているからね．唇やほっぺを咬まないようにね．2時まで食べちゃだめだよ．いいかい．
患児	わかった．
歯科医	そうだ．次も頑張ろうね．
患児	うん！
歯科医	お大事に．気をつけて帰ってね．バイバイ，ハナ．
患児	バイバイ！

アメリカの歯科事情4 －歯科検診システム－

アメリカの歯科検診は，6か月ごとに行います．児童では保健所や学校での歯科検診をするシステムはないので，個人でかかりつけの歯科医（主治医）に行って定期検診を受けなければいけません．主治医となる歯科医は一般歯科（General or Family Dentist）か小児歯科（Pediatric Dentist）です．

	hour so that she does not bite her lip and cheek.
Patient	Okay, I'll take care.
Dentist	Hana, your teeth and lip will be sleeping until 2 o'clock. Please do not bite your lip and cheek. No food until 2 o'clock. Okay?
Patient	Okay.
Dentist	Good girl. Will you be good next time, too?
Patient	Yes!
Dentist	Good. Take care, and have a safe trip home. Bye, Hana.
Patient	Bye!

レッスン9　矯正処置

○相談・初診時

アメリカ人男児9歳が母親とともに歯学部附属病院矯正歯科に来院した.

歯科医　歯並びがどうかされましたか？

母　親　アメリカにいるときに，かかりつけの歯医者さんから息子の上顎の前歯に問題があると指摘されました．主人が日本へ転勤になったので，こちらへ来てから治療を始めたいと考えていました．
　　　　どんな感じですか？　重大な問題がありますか？

歯科医　そうですねえ．ちょっと診てみましょう．
　　　　まず，あなたの息子さんの咬み合わせは，ご指摘されたように，上の歯列が下の歯列に比べて前に出ている咬み合わせです．

母　親　出っ歯ということですか？
　　　　でも，前歯は前突しているようには見えませんけど．

歯科医　おっしゃるとおりです．
　　　　息子さんの場合は，上顎前歯の唇側傾斜を伴わない上顎前突症例です．
　　　　これは，日本人と比べて欧米人に多く見られるタイプです．日本人で上顎前突といえば，上顎前歯の唇側傾斜を伴う上顎前突症例がほとんどです．

母　親　私も日本に来て，歯並びのわるいお子さんや出っ歯のお子さんが多いのには驚きました．

歯科医　あなたのお子さんは下あごの前方への成長が抑えられているように思われます．それで，下あごが小さく，位置も後方になっています．

母　親　治療はいつごろから始めればよいですか？

歯科医　治療の開始時期は症例によります．お子さんの場合はまだ混合歯列期ですが，まずは初期治療として，顎骨の整形治療から始めたほうがよいでしょう．

母　親　あごの矯正ですか？

歯科医　そのとおりです．まず，お子さんの頭部のエックス線写真を撮って，上あごと下あごの位置関係を調べます．
　　　　上顎前突と一口に言っても，いろいろなタイプがあります．
　　　　上あごの前後的な位置が正常でも下あごが後退した場合（下顎の劣成長）には，相対的に出っ歯となります．あごの骨にはまったく異常がなくて，前歯だけが前突してしまうという例もあります．
　　　　もし，上あごが過成長であれば，ヘッドギアを使う必要があります．逆に，下あごが劣成長であれば，下あごの成長を刺激し，前方誘導する装置を使う必要

LESSON 9 ORTHODONTIC TREATMENT

○ CONSULTATION · FIRST VISIT

An American boy, 9 years of age, came to the orthodontic department of university dental hospital with his mother.

Dentist   How can I help you?

Mother   When we were in the United States, our home dentist pointed out that my son's front teeth may be a problem. Since my husband was transferred to Japan, I've been considering having him treated here.
What do you think? Does he have a serious problem?

Dentist   Well, let's have a look. Hmm. I see.
First of all, the entire teeth of the upper jaw are positioned forward in relation to the lower dental arch.

Mother   You mean he has buckteeth, right?
But his front teeth don't seem to stick out.

Dentist   I know. You are right, Your son's case is not accompanied by forward tipping of the front teeth. Your son's type of malocclusion is more common among Caucasian people than Japanese people. In Japan most of the maxillary protrusion cases are accompanied by forward tipping of the front teeth.

Mother   I was surprised to see so many children with crowded teeth or projecting teeth since I came here.

Dentist   The forward growth of the lower jaw seems to be inhibited. That is to say, the lower jaw is small in size and is positioned more towards the back.

Mother   When is the best time for treatment?

Dentist   It depends on the case. In your son's case, there is a skeletal problem. Though the permanent teeth are not fully erupted yet, it's better to begin the orthopedic treatment of the jaws as an initial treatment.

Mother   Is it a correction of the jaws?

Dentist   Exactly. First of all, I have to take a cephalogram, an X-ray photograph of his face. Using this, I'll examine the positional relation of the jaws.
There are several types of maxillary protrusion. Mostly are cases in which the lower jaw is poorly grown with respect to the normal position of the upper jaw. There is also the case of only the front teeth's projection without abnormality of jaws.
In the case of excessive growth of the upper jaw, head gear should be worn. When the lower jaw is too far back, it should be displaced forward by stimulating the growth using a functional appliance. After that we observe the course of eruption of the per-

があります．その後，永久歯が生え代わるまで経過観察を行います．

母　親　それで治療は終わりますか？

歯科医　残念ながら，ほとんどの場合，永久歯がそろったときに，再び診断を行い，ブレースによる歯列矯正が始まります．これにはだいたい2年くらいかかります．矯正治療が終わった後には，歯の後戻りを防ぐための保定期間が3〜4年必要です．

母　親　長いお付き合いになりますねえ．

歯科医　そうですね．経過観察や保定期間を含めると長くなります．

母　親　どのくらいの間隔で通院が必要なのですか？

歯科医　月に1度定期的に通院していただく期間は実質的には3年程度です．経過観察や保定期間は3〜6か月に1度程度です．

母　親　何か心構えをすることがありますか？

歯科医　ヘッドギア，チンキャップ，ゴムなどの装置は，患者さんの協力が得られなければ効果が発揮できません．患者さんの協力が治療の成功には欠かせないのです．もちろん，お母さん方の協力も必要ですよ．

母　親　治療費用はどのくらいかかるのですか？

歯科医　料金は症例や治療期間によっても若干異なりますが，全治療期間を通してトータルで70万円くらいになると思います．
　　　　息子さんの治療を開始するかどうか，よくご検討ください．

母　親　わかりました．主人と相談してから，どうするかお知らせします．

○検査

母　親　先生に治療してもらうことにしました．

歯科医　承知しました．それでは，今日は上下の歯型をとったり，あごや歯並び全体のエックス線写真と，顔のエックス線写真，また口腔内や顔の写真を撮るなどの資料採得を行います．
　　　　その後，歯磨き指導も行いましょう．

母　親　ブレース装置をつけると，歯を磨きにくくなるのですか？

歯科医　そうです．ブレースは固定式の矯正装置ですから，当然，口腔内の衛生状態が悪化します．ですから，今まで以上に努力して歯を磨く習慣を身につけることが重要です．

○診断

歯科医　診断と治療計画ができましたので，詳細をご説明します．頭部エックス線規格写真計測の結果，やはり下あごが後退しているようです．

母　親　誰に似たのやら．遺伝でしょうか？

	manent teeth.
Mother	After that the orthodontic treatment is finished?
Dentist	I am afraid not. When permanent teeth are fully erupted, a diagnosis is made, and then orthodontic braces are worn in most patients. Treatment with braces requires about two years. Then it takes three to four years for the retention. A retainer will prevent any relapse after the braces are removed.
Mother	It's gonna be a long acquaintance isn't it?
Dentist	Yes, it is. It takes a long time including the period of observation and retention.
Mother	How often will we have to come to the clinic?
Dentist	You'll have to come once a month regularly for about three years, and once in every three to six months during the period of observation and retention.
Mother	Do we have to prepare anything for the treatment?
Dentist	Appliances such as head-gear, chin-cap and elastics never have good effects if the patient doesn't use them. A patient's cooperation is essential for the success of all treatments. Of course, the mother's cooperation is also necessary.
Mother	How much does the treatment cost?
Dentist	It depends on the case and treatment period. Total charge will be seven hundred thousand yen on an average. Please consider whether you want to have him treated or not, since you have your family to think about.
Mother	I understand. I'll let you know after I talk about it with my husband.

EXAMINATION

Mother	We've decided to have our son treated by you.
Dentist	All right. Then, today I'll take an impression of the upper and lower dental arches. X-ray photographs of the head, entire teeth and jaws, intraoral photographs and facial photographs will be also taken.
	And then tooth brushing instructions will be given as well.
Mother	Is it more difficult to brush teeth when braces are worn?
Dentist	Yes, because braces are fixed appliances, maintenance of good oral hygiene tends to be difficult. That is why it is important to make more effort to brush your teeth properly than before.

DIAGNOSIS

Dentist	I've made a diagnosis and treatment plan, I'll explain the details. The X-ray shows that the lower jaw is too far back.
Mother	I wonder which side of the family he gets his jaw from? Is it due to heredity?

歯科医　あごの形は遺伝などの先天的な要因が大きく影響しますが，絶対的なものではありません．つまり，後天的な要因を最大限に引き出せばよいのです．息子さんは成長しているので，うまく下あごの成長を刺激することができれば，前方に誘導してあげることは可能ですよ．

母　親　どんな装置を使うのですか？

歯科医　簡単に言えば，マウス・ピースみたいな装置です．これにより下あごの前方への成長を誘導してあげるのです．

アメリカの歯科事情 5　－歯科専門医制度－

アメリカでは，歯科の専門医が日本より細かく分かれています．いくつかの州では専門医にライセンスが必要になっています．そのために主治医は専門医の治療が必要な場合は，それぞれ専門の歯科医に紹介をする役割もあります．多くの場合，専門医の治療後，一般歯科の治療が必要となるため，直接専門医の所へ行っても，主治医がいない場合は主治医を見つけるよう勧められます．主な専門医は，矯正歯科医（Orthodontist），小児歯科医（Pediatric Dentist），歯内療法医（Endodontist），歯周病治療医（Periodontist），口腔外科医（Oral Surgeon），補綴専門医（Prosthodontist）です．

Dentist	The shape of jaw is greatly affected by congenital factors such as heredity, but not entirely dominated. That is to say, we can activate acquired factors. As your son is growing, it is possible to lead the lower jaw more forward if the growth of the lower jaw can be stimulated properly.
Mother	What kind of appliance should he wear?
Dentist	It's simply like a mouth piece. This activates the forward growth of the lower jaw.

レッスン10　審美歯科

ホワイトニング

○ 失活歯の漂白

患　者　前歯の色が黒くなってきてとても気になるのですが．

歯科医　この歯は以前治療を受けたことがありますか？

患　者　10年ぐらい前にむし歯になり神経を取って何か詰め物をしていたのですが，ここ2，3年，徐々に色が変わって目立つようになってきました．

歯科医　神経を取った歯は，全体的に透明感がなくなり次第に色が変化していくのです．また歯の隙間から，唾液や食べ物が入ったり食べ物の色素が入り込んだりして変色することもあります．
　　　　このような歯を白くする方法に漂白法があります．

患　者　どのような治療ですか？

歯科医　歯の漂白法とは，過酸化水素水と過ホウ酸ナトリウムという薬剤を用いて歯の中に貼付し1週間ごとに交換していきます．処置は変色の回復状態をみながら数回行います．

患　者　歯に対して何かわるいことはないですか？

歯科医　欠点として薬剤の影響で歯が脆くなることがあります．処置後に軽い知覚過敏を起こすこともありますが，持続性のあるものではありません．
　　　　どうされますか？

患　者　お願いします．

処置後

歯科医　いかがですか？　白くなった感じですか？

患　者　ずいぶんよくなりました．ありがとうございました．

歯科医　ホワイトニング効果は永続することが理想といえますが，現実には数々の要因が重なり「後戻り」といわれる改善後の色調変化が起こることもあります．少なくとも6か月間隔で定期検診に来ていただき，必要に応じてホワイトニングを行いつつ効果を維持させることをお勧めします．

○ オフィスホワイトニングとホームホワイトニング

患　者　近頃テレビでみる芸能人たちは，みんな歯の色が白くて綺麗ですよね．この歯科医院でも漂白をしているのでしょうか？

受　付　この診療所での歯の治療はすべて終わりましたので，これからはむし歯や歯周

LESSON 10 ESTHETIC DENTISTRY

WHITENING

○ WHITENING NON-VITAL TEETH

Patient   I'm very worried about this black part on my front tooth.

Dentist   Have you ever had this tooth treated before?

Patient   About ten years ago, I had the nerve in my tooth taken out and replaced. Gradually after two or three years, the change of tooth color has started to stand out.

Dentist   Generally, teeth with the nerve taken out lose the transparent look and the color changes gradually. Saliva and food particles in the spaces between the teeth gradually cause the teeth to become discolored, too.

Usually in this case I would bleach your tooth to make it look naturally white again.

Patient   Could you explain how you bleach the tooth?

Dentist   The bleaching method uses hydrogen peroxide solution and sodium perborate on the teeth once a week. Treatment usually takes several times depending on how fast the recovery of discoloration takes.

Patient   Isn't it bad for the teeth?

Dentist   Bleach medicine may make teeth weak with continual use over a period of time. Also, transitory slight hypersensitive perception might be caused after treatment, but those symptoms don't last. Do you want to try it?

Patient   OK, I will try it.

After whitening

Dentist   Well, what do you think? How do you feel about the color tone?

Patient   They look much better.

Thank you.

Dentist   Ideally, the effect of whitening will last a long time, but a lot of lifestyle factors can cause a change of color tone after treatment. I recommend that you have routine oral health checkups at least every six months in order to maintain the color and to have the whitening treatment again if necessary.

○ IN-OFFICE WHITENING AND HOME WHITENING

Patient   Recently, the actors and actresses on TV have very nice white teeth. Do you do whitening treatments in this dental clinic?

Staff   Yes, all teeth treatments are done at this clinic. We will continue your aftercare to pre-

審美歯科

病の予防を行っていく予定ですが，その中で自然な口元の美しさを目指すには漂白もよい方法ですよ．

患　者　へえ，そうなのですね．ちょっと具体的に話を聞いてみたいのですが．

受　付　わかりました．それでは担当の松下歯科衛生士に説明させましょう．

衛生士　こんにちは．まず歯を綺麗に保つには，普段の歯磨きにより歯や歯茎を健康にし，歯への着色や歯石を掃除することが大切です．その上で薬剤を用いて歯を白くしていくわけです．その方法には，診療室にて歯科医師が行うものと都合のよい時間にご自分が自宅で行うものとがあります．

患　者　診療室で行う方法はどのような内容ですか？

衛生士　歯科医師が，歯の表面に漂白するための薬を塗り，ハイパワーの器機を使用してレーザーなどの光を照射し処置します．数回来院していただけば，漂白完了後には白く美しい歯となります．

ただ残念なことに，現在の状態をご希望の白さまで改善できるという保証はありません．なぜかというと，生体にダメージを与えないよう，安全に漂白するには限界があるからです．またホワイトニング開始前に認識していただきたいことは，「人の目は敏感に新しい色調を認識できますが，自分の目はその色調にすぐに慣れてしまう」ことです．ご自分の歯を毎日見ていることで，白さが改善されても，以前から変化していないように錯覚しはじめます．もし効果に疑問を抱かれた場合は，歯科医師の保存する治療開始前のデータや写真と比較することで，疑問は解消されるはずです．

患　者　なるほど，よくわかりました．では自宅で行う方法はどうですか？

衛生士　あらかじめ患者さんの歯形からカスタムメイドのトレーを作ってお渡ししますので，そこへホワイトニング剤をご自身で入れていただき，あとは歯に装着することになります．この方法がホームホワイトニングです．

患　者　あと治療期間や料金はどうなりますか？

衛生士　オフィスホワイトニングの場合は，漂白する歯の数によって若干異なりますが，通常1回30分〜1時間程度の治療時間が必要です．必要に応じて約1週間間隔で4回処置しますが，早ければ1回の来院で，通常は2〜3回の来院で十分な治療効果が得られます．健康保険適用外の治療となりますので，1歯あたり6,380円です．代金は，3回目の処置後にいただきます．

またホームホワイトニングの場合は，決められた量の薬剤を入れたトレーを1日2時間装着します．装用期間は2週間です．簡単ですが，患者さんご自身の努力が治療効果に影響します．注意事項としては，押し出された薬剤を飲み込んでいると，のどに痛みを感じることがありますので，吐き出すようにしてください．トレーを使用した後は，水洗・乾燥させてトレーケースに入れ，清潔に保管するよう心がけてください．また，トレーは熱で変形しますので，熱湯

	vent decays and gum diseases. It is good to do whitening to enhance the natural beauty of your teeth.
Patient	All right, I would like to have a consultation about that.
Staff	Sure, I will ask D.H. Matsushita to explain you about teeth whitening.
D.H.	Hi, how are you. To keep your teeth clean, it is important to clean your teeth and gum. At the same time, teeth whitening is conducted. There are two ways to bleach the teeth. One is in-office whitening and the other one is home whitening.
Patient	What do you do for in-office whitening?
D.H.	The dentist will put whitening agents on your teeth surface and apply high energy light such as the laser on the teeth. You need to visit us several times to get white teeth. Unfortunately, it is not guaranteed that we will obtain the precise results that you expect. This is because there is a limit to how much we can whiten the teeth without damaging the teeth and organism. Furthermore, although humans can easily detect a new color, we get accustomed to the new color very quickly. Therefore, you may not feel such a big change or improvement in the color because you check your teeth everyday. If you can't see the difference in color before and after the treatment, you should ask the doctor to show you the data and pictures before and after the treatment so that you can compare. Then, you will be able to see the evidence for yourself and hopefully you will be satisfied with the improvements.
Patient	I see, how about home whitening?
D.H.	First, we will make you your own custom-made tray that we will make from a model of your mouth. You need to put whitening agents on the tray and place it in your mouth at home.
Patient	How long does it take and how much does it cost?
D.H.	In-office whitening, it depends on the number of the teeth to be whitened. You are charged per tooth. Usually, it takes about half an hour to one hour for a weekly treatment. There will be four treatments maximum. You can tell the color change after one treatment in some cases. However, it usually takes two to three treatments for optimal results. Whitening treatment is not covered by insurance. You will need to pay 6,380 yen per tooth. We will charge you after the third treatment. For home whitening, you need to use a custom-made tray with a whitening agent for two hours per day and two weeks total. The effectiveness of whitening depends on your effort. You need to be careful not to swallow the whitening agent since it might cause a sore throat. Be sure to spit out the whitening agent if it collects in your mouth. After you use the tray, wash and dry it. It should be kept clean in the carrying case.

　　　　　で洗浄しないようご注意ください．トレーを装着したままでの飲食は，厳禁です．
　　　　　またホワイトニング中は再着色の原因となる嗜好品や飲食物（タバコ・コーヒー・ウーロン茶・赤ワイン・ケチャップ・カレーなど）の摂取を控えるほうが無難です．
　　　　　料金については，1顎あたり30,000円です．代金は，初回の処置後にいただきます．さらに薬剤を追加する場合は，8,000円いただきます．
患　者　いろいろと説明していただきありがとうございました．それでは次回の来院時に返事をします．

アメリカの歯科事情6　－審美歯科－

> アメリカでは，「歯が汚い人は生活習慣のわるい人，生活のレベルが低い人」とみなされがちで，歯並びをきれいにする矯正や，歯を白くするホワイトニングが盛んに行われています．矯正歯科治療では誰でも一生に1回だけ保険がききます．ホワイトニングでは，日本では歯科医院でしか使えないほどの強力な薬剤付のホワイトニングキットを一般の薬局で手に入れることができます．

Don't put the tray into hot water since the heat will distort it. Also, don't eat and drink during the application.

You also need to avoid tobacco, coffee, tea, red wine, ketchup and curry.

The home whitening fee is about 30,000 yen per upper or lower arch. We will charge after the first treatment. Fee for extra agents is about 8,000 yen.

Patient   Thank you very much for you kind explanation. I will let you know whether I will take the treatment or not at next appointment.

check your teeth everyday...

ポーセレンラミネートベニア修復

○初診日
歯科医　ロバートさんですね．はじめまして，村瀬です．
　　　　どうなさいましたか？
患　者　実は，上の前歯の色が気になるんです．
歯科医　いつ頃からですか？
患　者　もともと小さい頃からです．
歯科医　そうしたらラミネートベニアがいいでしょうね．
患　者　それは何ですか？
歯科医　2回かかるんですが，1回目に前歯6本の唇側を薄く削って型をとります．そして次の回に薄いセラミックスの板を接着して終わりです．だいたい1週間ほどかかりますが，その間は仮歯もできます．

患　者　なるほど．それでお願いします．

○支台歯形成，色調採得，印象
歯科医　こんにちは，ロバートさん．今日は，上の前歯6本を少し削りますね．
患　者　痛くないですか？
歯科医　大丈夫，痛くないですよ．
　　　　では，イスを倒します．お口を開けてください．
支台歯形成後
歯科医　はい，削るのはこれで終わりです．どうぞ，うがいをしてください．
　　　　（衛生士に向かって）A2とA3のシェードガイドと一緒に歯の写真を撮ってください．
衛生士　はい，先生．
色調採得後
歯科医　では型をおとりします．
印象採得後
歯科医　最後に仮歯をつくりましょう．
患　者　先生，1週間くらいなら，仮歯は結構です．
歯科医　そうですか，では今日はこれで終わりです．
患　者　ありがとうございました．

○ラミネートベニアの装着
歯科医　こんにちは．調子はどうですか？

ESTHETIC DENTISTRY

PROSTHODONTIC TREATMENT USING PORCELAIN LAMINATE VENEER

◯ THE FIRST VISIT

Dentist   Nice to meet you, Mrs. Roberts. I am Murase.
What seems to be the trouble?

Patient   Well, the color of my upper front tooth worries me.

Dentist   When did you find it?

Patient   It's natural. It's been this way since I was a child.

Dentist   Let me see. I think laminate veneer is suitable.

Patient   What is it?

Dentist   It takes two appointments. In the first appointment, I'll trim the labial surface of the six front teeth like a peeling, and then take an impression. In the next appointment, I'll bond thin ceramic veneers on the teeth. That's it. It takes about one week to make the ceramic veneers. Temporary restorations are available in the mean time.

Patient   I see.

◯ TOOTH PREPARATION, SHADE TAKING, AND IMPRESSION

Dentist   Good afternoon, Mrs. Roberts. Today, I'll grind the six front teeth slightly.

Patient   Is it painful?

Dentist   Don't worry. There will be no pain.
I'll tilt the seat. Please open your mouth.

After the tooth preparation

Dentist   Preparation is completed now. Please rinse your mouth.
(To D.H.) Please take some pictures of these teeth with shade guides A2 and A3 together.

D.H.   Yes, Doctor.

After the shade taking

Dentist   Let's take an impression now.

After taking the impression

Dentist   Finally, I'll make a temporary restoration.

Patient   Doctor, I don't need the temporary restoration since there will only be one week.

Dentist   OK. Then, today's treatment is finished.

Patient   Thank you very much.

◯ FIX THE LAMINATE VENEER

Dentist   Good afternoon. How are you today.

患　者　はい，お陰さまで．
歯科医　これができあがったセラミックスです．さっそく合わせてみましょう．
　　　　（衛生士に向かって）エステティックセメントを使います．ベニアにトライインペーストを塗ってください．
　　　　鏡をどうぞ．ラミネートベニアを試しに付けていますが，いかがですか？
患　者　うわー，いいですね．
歯科医　では接着材でくっつけましょう．
　　　　（衛生士に向かって）ベニアを清掃して，リン酸処理して，シランカップリング剤を塗布してください．セメントの色はユニバーサルがいいです．

衛生士　はい，準備できました．
歯科医　表面を処理しますよ．
　　　　（衛生士に向かって）では一枚ずつベニアを接着します．セメントを練ってください．はい，光を当ててください．

ラミネートベニアの装着後
歯科医　それでは，イスを起こします．お口をゆすいで，鏡をどうぞご覧ください．
患　者　きれいになってよかったです．
歯科医　セラミックスは歯よりも欠けやすいので，前歯では物を嚙み切らないようにしてください．ブラッシングは今まで通り，歯ブラシや糸ようじが使えます．

患　者　先生どうもありがとうございました．
歯科医　どういたしまして．

Patient	I am good.
Dentist	Here are the fabricated veneers. Let's try to fit them in.
	(To D.H.) I want to use the Esthetic Cement. Please apply the try-on paste on the laminate veneers.
	Please hold this mirror, and we'll try on the laminate veneers. What do you think?
Patient	Oh my goodness, I like them.
Dentist	OK. Let's bond it with an adhesive now.
	(To D.H.) Please clean the ceramic veneers, condition the surface with phosphoric acid, and then prime with the silane coupler. The color of the luting agent should be Universal.
D.H.	Yes, I am ready.
Dentist	I'll condition the tooth surface.
	(To D.H.) From now, I'll bond the ceramics one by one. Please mix the luting agent. Light cure now, please.

After the laminate veneers have set

Dentist	OK. I will bring the chair up. Please rinse your mouth, and have a look in this mirror.
Patient	They look great. I am really happy.
Dentist	When compared to the natural tooth, the ceramics is relatively brittle. So, please be careful not to bite any food off with your front teeth. When brushing, you can use your toothbrush and dental floss as usual.
Patient	Thank you very much, Doctor.
Dentist	You are welcome. It's my pleasure.

レッスン11　顎関節症

　　歯科医　ウエイドさん，こんにちは．どうしました？
　　患　者　痛くて，口が開けられないのです．
　　歯科医　最初にあごの関節が変な感じになったのはいつですか？
　　患　者　よく覚えていませんが，5〜6年前だったと思います．
　　　　　　朝，食事をしていて，口を開けるときに左のあごの関節で音がしたのです．
　　　　　　それから，口を開けるときはいつも音がするようになりました．
　　歯科医　わかりました．痛みを感じたのはいつからですか？
　　患　者　2週間前です．朝食事をするとき，突然痛くなりました．
　　歯科医　いつ口が開けにくいと感じましたか？
　　患　者　痛くなった日です．
　　歯科医　痛みは強くなっていますか？
　　患　者　痛み始めて2〜3日は大変痛かったのですが，今は少しよくなりました．
　　　　　　でも，まだ大きく口を開けることができません．
　　歯科医　音がし始める前に，顔やあごを打った経験がありますか？
　　患　者　はっきりとは覚えていませんが，多分なかったと思います．
　　歯科医　ウエイドさん，歯ぎしりすると言われたことはありますか？
　　患　者　いいえ，ありません．
　　歯科医　全身のことについてお聞きします．
　　　　　　関節リウマチや膠原病で治療を受けたことがありますか？
　　患　者　いいえ，ありません．
　　歯科医　それでは，検査しましょう．

顎関節部を触診しながら
　　歯科医　痛いですか？
　　患　者　左がすごく痛いです．
　　歯科医　すごく痛そうですね．
　　　　　　では，ゆっくり口が開くところまで開けください．
　　患　者　先生，もう痛くてこれ以上開けられません．
　　歯科医　わかりました．
　　　　　　さて，あごの関節のレントゲンとMRIを撮って，調べましょう．

エックス線写真を見ながら
　　歯科医　ウエイドさん，エックス線写真を見てください．
　　　　　　この骨が下顎頭で，この窪みが関節窩です．
　　　　　　左の下顎頭の部分が，少しすり減っています．

LESSON 11 TEMPOROMANDIBULAR JOINT DISORDERS

Dentist　Hi. Ms Wade. What can I do for you?

Patient　It is hard to open my mouth widely, because it hurts.

Dentist　When did you first notice the unpleasant feeling?

Patient　I don't know exactly, maybe five or six years ago.

　　　　When I ate breakfast and opened my mouth, the jaw on the left side sounded strange.

　　　　Since then, my jaw doesn't sound natural when I open my mouth.

Dentist　I see. When did the pain start?

Patient　Two weeks ago. While I was eating breakfast, it suddenly started to hurt.

Dentist　When did you feel it difficult to open your mouth?

Patient　The day when I felt the pain.

Dentist　Is the pain stronger now?

Patient　It was very painful for two days. It's a little better now.

　　　　But I still can't open my mouth widely.

Dentist　Before the symptoms started, were you hit in the face or the jaw?

Patient　I don't remember exactly, I don't think so.

Dentist　Ms Wade, have you ever been told that you grind your teeth?

Patient　No, I haven't.

Dentist　I'd like to ask you about your medical history. Have you ever received medical treatment for rheumatoid arthritis or collagen disease?

Patient　No, I haven't.

Dentist　Well, let me see.

In palpating her temporomandibular region

Dentist　Do you feel any pain?

Patient　It's very painful on the left.

Dentist　The pain looks severe.

　　　　So, please open your mouth gently and as widely as possible.

Patient　I can't open my mouth any more.

Dentist　I see.

　　　　First, well, let's take an X-ray and MRI of the jaw and check it out.

In showing X-ray dental film

Dentist　Ms Wade, please look at the X-ray film.

　　　　This bone is the mandibular head and this hollow is the mandibular fossa.

　　　　It looks like the left mandibular head is slightly worn away.

	歯ぎしりが原因かもしれません．
	つぎに，MRIをみてください．
	左の関節円板が前方にずれています．
	口が大きく開かないのは，恐らくこれが原因だと思います．
患　者	どうして，円板が前にずれたのでしょうか？
歯科医	原因は今のところ，はっきりしていません．
	歯ぎしり，打撲や生活習慣とかいろいろなことが原因と言われています．
	ストレスも重大な原因と言われています．
患　者	咬み合わせがこの病気の原因なのですか？
歯科医	現状では，あまり重大な原因とは言われていません．
	顎関節症の治療としては，通常スプリントを入れます．
	約2週間ごとにスプリントの調整をします．
患　者	私の場合は？
歯科医	ウエイドさんの場合には，痛みが強く，口が大きく開きませんので，まずは，
	鎮痛剤や電気マッサージをして，痛みを少しでも軽減します．
	その後，スプリントを入れます．
	2か月くらいで，ほとんどの症状がなくなります．
	しかし約10%の人は，まったくスプリントがきかないことがあります．
患　者	そのときは，どういう治療をするのですか？
歯科医	この空隙に注射して，関節を洗浄したり，バンピングと呼ばれる処置をします．
患　者	バンピングとはどんな治療ですか？
歯科医	麻酔液などの注射により，関節の空隙を大きくしたり，洗浄したりする治療です．
患　者	痛くないですか？
歯科医	麻酔をしますから，ほとんど痛みはないと思います．
患　者	処置は保険でやれますか？
歯科医	はい，もちろんできます．スプリントで，2〜3か月すればほとんどの症状はとれますよ．
患　者	わかりました．よろしくお願いします．

	This cause is probably a bruxism.
	Well then, please look at the MRI.
	It looks like the left articular disk is slipping ahead.
	This is probably the reason that you can't open your mouth widely.
Patient	Why did the disk slip ahead?
Dentist	Its cause is not clear at the present time. Several things could be the cause. For example, bruxism, bruise, life style, and so on.
	Stress is also said to be an important cause.
Patient	Is a bite condition causing the problem?
Dentist	It isn't said that a bite condition is a serious cause at present. A splint is usually put in the mouth for treatment of temporomandibular disorders. I usually adjust the splint every other week.
Patient	Oh, how will you treat my case?
Dentist	In your case, Ms Wade, the pain is severe, and it is difficult to open your mouth widely. At first, the pain should be relieved by a pain-reliever or by giving electronic massage. I will put a splint in your mouth after that. Most of the symptoms will go away after about 2 months. However, the splint therapy isn't always effective. About 10% don't show any improvement.
Patient	What would you do in that case?
Dentist	We will do an injection into the space here to wash it out and maybe do a treatment called bumping manipulation.
Patient	What is the treatment of bumping manipulation?
Dentist	This therapy is enlarging a space of the joint and washing out the joint by an injection such as an anesthetic.
Patient	Is that painful?
Dentist	You don't feel any pain because of the anesthetic.
Patient	This treatment will be covered by my insurance, right?
Dentist	Yes, That's right. Most symptoms will disappear with splint therapy after two or three months.
Patient	Great, thank you very much.

レッスン 12　摂食嚥下リハビリテーション

○問診

歯科医　食事の際にむせることはありますか？
患　者　ときどきむせることがあり食事に時間がかかります．
歯科医　のどに詰まる感じはありませんか？
患　者　固形物を食べると，ときどき詰まってしまい，しばらくは残っているようです．
歯科医　摂取量の低下や体重の減少はありませんか？
患　者　2か月前から食べにくく感じるようになり，今では以前の半分しか食べられません．体重もこの2か月で5kg減少しました．
歯科医　発熱したり肺炎になったりしたことはありませんか？
患　者　肺炎になったことはありませんが，ここ数日間微熱が続いています．

○診査

歯科医　口笛を吹くように唇を前方に突き出してください．
　　　　舌を前に出してください．
　　　　声を「アー」と出してください．
　　　　唾液を飲み込む検査を行います．30秒間計りますので，できるだけ多く唾液を飲み込んでください．3ccの水を口に入れますので，いつもどおりに飲み込んでください．

○検査

歯科医　嚥下内視鏡の検査について説明します．
　　　　鼻から細いカメラを入れて，のどを観察します．次にカメラを入れながら少量の検査食を摂取していただきます．食べ物を飲み込む際に，食べ物が誤って気管に入ることを誤嚥と言いますが，内視鏡検査では誤嚥の有無だけでなく，咽頭への送り込み機能や気管の閉鎖状態，嚥下反射の異常，嚥下後の残留状態などを評価することができます．
患　者　痛くはないのでしょうか？
歯科医　違和感はありますがそれほど痛いものではありません．
　　　　嚥下造影検査ではバリウム入りの検査食を摂取しながら，エックス線透視装置を用いて飲み込む様子を評価します．口腔内で食塊を作る様子や咽頭への送り込み，嚥下にかかわる舌骨という骨の動きや気管の閉鎖状態，嚥下反射のタイミング，咽頭残留や食道通過の状況などが評価でき，誤嚥の有無に関しても詳

LESSON 12 DYSPHAGIA REHABILITATION

○ CONSULTATION

Dentist	Do you have difficulty swallowing food?
Patient	Yes. Sometimes I feel like I'm choking. It takes a long time for me to eat.
Dentist	Do you sometimes feel that food gets stuck in your throat?
Patient	Solid food sometimes gets stuck in my throat, and remains for a while.
Dentist	Have you experienced a decrease in appetite or weight?
Patient	I started having difficulties in eating over the last 2 months, and I can eat only half of what I used to. I lost 5kg of weight over the last 2 months.
Dentist	Have you had a fever or pneumonia?
Patient	I didn't have pneumonia, but I have had a slight fever over the last couple of days.

○ EXAMINATION

Dentist　Please stick out your lips like when you blow a whistle.

　　　　　Stick out your tongue next.

　　　　　Please say "Ah" loudly.

　　　　　Next, I'm going to ask you to do the saliva swallowing test. Please swallow as much saliva as possible in 30 seconds.

　　　　　Here is 3cc of water.

　　　　　Please drink it when I place it in your mouth.

○ TEST

Dentist　I am going to explain about the Video Endoscopic Evaluation of Swallowing.

　　　　　A small camera is inserted into the nose to observe the throat. Then, the patient is instructed to swallow a small amount of test food while the camera is in place. Aspiration occurs when food accidentally enters the larynx while swallowing. The endoscope can evaluate aspiration, transportation of food or liquids to the throat, larynx occlusion, any abnormal swallowing reflex, and residue after swallowing.

Patient　Is the procedure painful?

Dentist　There is some discomfort, but it's not painful.

　　　　　In the Video fluoroscopic Examination of Swallowing, test food including barium is given, and the movement of the throat is evaluated. This test evaluates the process of forming a Bolus in the mouth, transportation to the throat, the movement of the hyoid bone, which is responsible for swallowing, the status of larynx occlusion, timing of

細な評価が可能です.

○ 診断と説明

歯科医 加齢とともに飲み込む力が低下したため，食べ物がのどに残りやすい状態になっています．残った食べ物が，新たに取り込んだ食べ物と一緒になることでのどの許容量を超えてしまい，結果的に気管への流れ込みが起きます．このように食べ物などが気管に入ることを誤嚥と言います．誤嚥が原因で肺炎を起こす場合があり，これを誤嚥性肺炎と言います．

患　者 何か治療が必要でしょうか？

歯科医 飲み込みにかかわる筋肉を鍛える目的でのリハビリが必要です．
脳血管障害の影響により，口唇や舌の運動麻痺がみられます．そのため，食塊形成や送り込み機能が低下しており，食事に時間がかかり，誤嚥を生じやすい状態です．

患　者 通常の食事をとってもよいのでしょうか？

歯科医 しばらくはトロミ食をとる必要があります．
嚥下機能が低下しているため，経口摂取だけでは十分な栄養補給ができません．

患　者 口から食べられないのであれば，どうすればよいのでしょうか？

歯科医 胃に直接栄養剤を送る「胃瘻栄養」を行うことが望ましいと考えます．

○ 対処法

衛生士 口腔および咽頭周囲にある嚥下関連筋の筋力増強を目的として，口腔周囲のマッサージや頸部運動訓練を行います．

患　者 毎日行うのでしょうか？

衛生士 自宅で毎日行ってください．
直接食べる訓練を行います．嚥下訓練用のゼリーを用いて一口量を小スプーン1杯に定めます．口に入れたら確実に飲み込むのを確認してから次の摂取を行います．

患　者 むせる場合はどうすればよいでしょうか？

衛生士 中止して，咳払いを十分に行ってください．
誤嚥を防止する目的で，液体にはすべてトロミをつける必要があります．

患　者 どのくらいのトロミをつければよいのでしょうか？

衛生士 トロミの濃度は3％が適当ですので，100ccの液体にトロミ剤を3g入れて，かき混ぜてください．

the swallowing reflex, food debris in the throat, and esophageal transit. It is considered to be a very precise method for examining aspiration.

◯ DIAGNOSIS AND EXPLANATION

Dentist It becomes more difficult to swallow food as you get older, and residual food tends to remain in the throat. When you eat something while residual food from the previous bite still remains in the throat, it exceeds the capacity of the throat, causing food flux into the larynx. Aspiration occurs when the food enters the larynx. Pneumonia caused by aspiration is called "aspiration pneumonia".

Patient How do you treat it?

Dentist Rehabilitation to enhance the swallowing-related muscles is necessary.
Palsy of lips and tongue are observed due to the influence of cerebrovascular disorder. This causes the dysfunction of forming Bolus and transportation, and, therefore, it takes more time to eat, and tends to cause aspiration.

Patient Can I eat normal food?

Dentist Actually, I recommend adding a thickener to liquefied food.
Due to swallowing dysfunction, you cannot get enough nutrition orally.

Patient What will I do if I can't eat and swallow food?

Dentist It is ideal to provide nutrition through a "stomach fistula".

◯ TREATMENT

D.H. Massage and cervical muscle training are necessary to enhance the swallowing-related muscles around the mouth and throat.

Patient How often should I do the massage and training?

D.H. It is recommended to give massage and training every day at home.
Food intake training is also necessary. Please take a spoonful of jelly in the mouth for swallowing training. Make sure the jelly in the mouth is fully swallowed before giving the next spoonful.

Patient What should I do if I keep coughing?

D.H. You should stop training, and clear the throat.
All liquid should be condensed to avoid aspiration.

Patient How thick should I condense the liquid?

D.H. Please add 3grams of thickener per 100cc of liquid since the appropriate concentration is 3%.

レッスン 13　特殊な歯科処置

○診査

狭心症を有する患者が歯痛を主訴として受診した．

歯科医　どうなさいました．

患　者　冷たい飲み物を飲むと，しみるのです．厄介なことに私には狭心症がありまして，たいていの先生は私の診察に慎重です．

歯科医　なるほど，では狭心症のケアをされる主治医はいらっしゃるのですか？

患　者　ええ，ケント先生が管理されています．

歯科医　それは結構なことです．歯の症状が深刻でなければ，ケント先生に連絡を取って診療上参考になることを聞いておきましょう．でも，まずは今の状態を調べましょう．

歯科医は検査を完了し，診断を下す．結論として，歯に大きなう窩があり，歯の神経（歯髄）に近接していた．そのため，冷たい飲み物が歯の神経を刺激して，痛みがあった．歯の神経の炎症と歯痛を予防するため，歯科医はう窩を暫間材料で封鎖した．

歯科医　左下の臼歯にむし歯があります．幸い，歯の神経を取る必要はありません．修復処置で十分だと思います．

患　者　よかった．治療上，注射は必要ですか？

歯科医　必要です．削れば痛みがあります．それで，歯の神経の感覚を鈍くし麻痺させるために麻酔薬を使います．

患　者　注射は嫌いです．とても怖い．

歯科医　大丈夫．特別な塗り薬がありまして，注射の痛みを和らげてくれます．注射の直前に注射する場所に塗ります．それでうまくいきますよ．

患　者　心疾患に対して注射はどんな影響がありますか？

歯科医　いい質問ですね．一般に注射を含むすべての歯科診療によって患者さんの血圧は上がり，ストレスがかかります．しかし，私どもは心電図を含むモニター装置を持っております．この装置の助けで重要な徴候を見つけ，重大な状態を避けられます．

患　者　それで何をみるのですか？

歯科医　5分ごとに血圧を測定します．さらに脈拍数および血液中の酸素飽和度もモニターします．これらの徴候の変化に注意を払います．とりわけ90％まで下が

LESSON 13 SPECIAL DENTAL TREATMENT

EXAMINATION

A patient with angina pectoris complains of a toothache and visits a dental office.

Dentist   What can I do for you?

Patient   My tooth hurts when I have cold drinks.
          The problem is that I also have angina pectoris.
          Consequently, most dentists hesitate to treat me.

Dentist   I see. Do you have a doctor who is treating your disease?

Patient   Yes, I do. Dr. Kent is my doctor.

Dentist   That's good. If the symptoms are not so serious, I'll contact Dr. Kent to get any useful information for treatment. But, first, I would like to see the present condition.

The dentist completed his examination and made a diagnosis. The conclusion was that the patient's tooth had a deep cavity close to the nerves. Consequently, cold drinks stimulated the tooth nerves and he felt pain. The dentist filled the hole with a temporary sealing material to prevent inflammation of the tooth nerve and a toothache.

Dentist   You have a cavity in a lower left molar. I don't think that the tooth nerve has to be removed. Restoration is enough for your tooth.

Patient   That's good. In order to treat my tooth, do you need to do any injections?

Dentist   Yes. Drilling often causes pain. So we use a painkiller to desensitize or paralyze tooth nerves.

Patient   I don't like injections. I'm very scared of needles.

Dentist   Don't worry. We have a special paste, that reduces pain. Just before injection, we put it on the injection site. It will work perfectly in your case.

Patient   How are the effects of injections on heart diseases?

Dentist   That is a good question. In general, all dental procedures including injections raise patient's blood pressure and cause some stress. We have monitoring devices including an electrocardiogram. This device helps us to watch for significant signs or symptoms and to avoid any serious problems.

Patient   How does it work?

Dentist   We can measure your blood pressure every 5 minutes. In addition, we can monitor your pulse rate and oxygen saturation in blood, which allows us to pay a lot of atten-

るような酸素飽和度の下降は血液中の酸素の供給が不十分であることを意味しますので，大変重要な徴候です．

患　者　モニターには針を使うのですか？痛いですか？

歯科医　まったく問題ありません．針を使わないし，痛くもないと思いますよ．片腕に血圧測定用のバンドを巻いて，反対の手の指にパルスメーター用のセンサーを装着します．ですから，モニタリングで痛むことはありません．しかし，心疾患をもつ患者さんでは，ときに歯科治療がもとで発作が起こることがあります．いくつかお尋ねします．

患　者　いいですよ．

歯科医　最近，発作はありましたか？

患　者　ありません．2年前にはありました．それでケント先生のところへ行き，ニトログリセリンや血圧を下げる薬をもらいました．それからは発作も減り，今ではほとんどありません．

歯科医　その薬をお持ちですか？

患　者　ええ，持っていますよ．

歯科医　歯科診療を受けるのに大きな問題はないと思いますが，今までの状態を主治医に確認しておきます．よろしいですか？

患　者　どうぞ．

歯科医　ケント先生の電話番号をお教えください．

患　者　ここに予約カードがあります．これに書いてあると思います．

歯科医　たしかに．どうも．今日はこれでおしまいです．次回の予約を決めましょう．

	tion to any changes. Especially, a fall in oxygen saturation under 90% means insufficient oxygen supplies in blood. So, it is a very important sign.
Patient	Do you use any needles for monitoring? Does it hurt?
Dentist	Not at all. We don't use any needles. In fact you might not feel any pain at all. We put the band for measuring blood pressure on one of your arms and the sensor for a pulse meter on a finger of the other hand. Therefore, it doesn't hurt at all. In some patients with heart disease, a heart attack results from stress during dental treatment. I would like to ask you a few questions.
Patient	Sure, go ahead.
Dentist	Recently, have you had a heart attack?
Patient	No. Two years ago, I had an attack. Then, I visited Dr. Kent and got nitroglycerin and a depressor. Since then, the frequency of attacks has decreased.
Dentist	Do you have nitroglycerin with you?
Patient	Yes, I have it at all times.
Dentist	OK. I don't think that we will have any major problems. Anyway, I'll confirm your medical history with your doctor. OK?
Patient	Sure.
Dentist	Can I have Dr. Kent's phone number?
Patient	Here is Dr. Kent's appointment card. You will find it on the card.
Dentist	OK. That's fine. Thank you. Today, this is all we have to do. Now, we will make your next appointment.

レッスン 14　口腔外科と歯科麻酔処置

○ **外傷**
患　者　1時間前に転んで，前歯を打ったのです．
歯科医　痛いですか？
患　者　ズキズキしています．
歯科医　診せてください．あまり出血はしていませんね．でも，前歯の2本が大変ぐらぐらしています．まずは，レントゲンを撮りましょう．

エックス線写真を見ながら
歯科医　上顎の骨は折れていません．しかし，前歯の2本は脱臼しています．
患　者　脱臼といいますと？
歯科医　歯が骨の窪みから飛び出している状態です．
患　者　この2本はどうなるのでしょうか？
歯科医　すぐには抜歯はしませんが，歯の神経を取らなければいけないでしょうね．
患　者　ずいぶん揺れていますけど，収まるでしょうか？
歯科医　隣の歯に接着剤で固定します．炎症が治って，土台の骨がうまく治れば固定するでしょう．
患　者　固定してこなければどうなりますか？
歯科医　残念ですが，抜歯ということになります．
患　者　抜歯すれば，その後はどうなりますか？
歯科医　隣の歯を削って，ブリッジにします．前歯ですから，歯と同じ色の冠が保険でできます．
　　　　今日は消毒して，隣の歯と接着剤で固定しましょう．消炎剤と抗生物質，鎮痛剤を出しますので飲んでください．
　　　　それから，遅かれ早かれ歯の神経をとります．
　　　　そうしないと，歯の神経に炎症が起こって痛くなりますよ．
患　者　わかりました．なるべく歯を抜かないようにお願いします．

○ **智歯周囲炎**
患　者　2～3日前から右下の親知らずが痛いのです．ズキズキして，昨日はあまり眠れませんでした．
歯科医　診てみましょう．親知らずの周りが大変腫れています．歯と歯茎の間に膿も溜

LESSON 14 ORAL SURGICAL TRETMANET & DENTAL ANESTHESIA

○ AN INJURY

Patient   I had a bad fall about an hour ago, I really hit my front teeth hard.

Dentist   Do you feel pain?

Patient   Yeah. It hurts a lot. It's really painful!

Dentist   Please show me. There is not so much bleeding.

               The front two teeth are very loose.

               First, let's take an X-ray.

In showing the X-ray films.

Dentist   Your upper jaw is not broken. But, the two front teeth are dislocated.

Patient   What do you mean?

Dentist   The teeth have come out of the dental bone sockets.

Patient   How do I get them back in?

Dentist   I won't pull out these teeth right away. But I have to take out the dental nerve.

Patient   My front teeth feel very loose. Are they OK?

Dentist   I'll fix the loose teeth to the next teeth with an adhesive agent.

               If inflammation disappears, and the bone heals, these teeth will be OK.

Patient   What if there is a problem?

Dentist   I'm sorry, but I'll have to pull out the teeth.

Patient   If the teeth are pulled out, what will be the next treatment?

Dentist   I'll grind the teeth next to these teeth, and set a bridge. As they are front teeth, the crowns with tooth color are covered by insurance. Today, I'll wash the teeth, and secure the loose teeth to the teeth next to them. I'll give you an antiphlogistic, an antibiotic and a painkiller. And then, I'll have to take out the nerve sooner or later.

               If I don't take out the nerve, the nerve will become inflamed, and these teeth will continue to cause you pain.

Patient   I see. If possible, please don't pull out the teeth.

○ PERICORONITIS OF THE WISDOM TOOTH

Patient   My lower right wisdom tooth started to hurt about two or three days ago. The tooth was throbbing, so I couldn't sleep well last night.

Dentist   OK, let's have a look. The gum around the wisdom tooth is swollen. There is pus be-

　　　　　まっています．さらにわるいことに親知らずには深いむし歯があります．
患　者　痛みはとれるでしょうか？
歯科医　すぐではないでしょうが，とれるでしょう．まず親知らずと歯茎の間の食べか
　　　　すを取ります．むし歯の部分には仮の詰め物をします．そして歯茎を消毒しま
　　　　す．あとは，消炎剤，抗生物質，鎮痛剤を飲んでください．
患　者　それで親知らずはどうなりますか？
歯科医　歯茎の炎症が治れば，抜歯します．
患　者　炎症はどれくらいで治るでしょうか？
歯科医　腫れは2〜3日は続くかもしれません．しかし，痛みは明日には収まるでしょ
　　　　う．そうすると来週ぐらいには抜歯できるでしょう．
　　　　　明日でも明後日でも差し支えないので，時間がとれるときに，消毒に来てくだ
　　　　さい．では，お大事に．

C 抜歯

患　者　昨日夕御飯を食べていたら，冠が取れました．
歯科医　取れた冠は持っていますか？
患　者　はい．これです．
歯科医　冠と歯と一緒に取れていますね．
患　者　つけ直せますか？
歯科医　残念ですが，残っている歯の虫食いが
　　　　大きいので，つけ直すのは無理ですし，
　　　　抜歯しなければいけません．
患　者　そうですか．残念です．
歯科医　歯茎が少し腫れていますので今日は抜きません．消毒をします．
　　　　化膿止め，腫れ止めと鎮痛剤を出しますので，飲んでください．

次回来院時

歯科医　カーターさん，歯茎の腫れが引きましたので，今日抜歯します．最近血圧は測
　　　　りましたか？
患　者　測ってないけど，高くはないと思いますよ．
歯科医　まあ，一応念のために測りましょう．125と80です．いいようですね．今まで，
　　　　出血が止まりにくいことがありましたか？
患　者　いいえ．
歯科医　今，ほかの病院にかかっていますか？
患　者　いいえ．
歯科医　鎮痛剤やペニシリン，注射などへのアレルギーはありますか？　あるいは薬の

ORAL SURGICAL TRETMANET & DENTAL ANESTHESIA

tween the gum and the tooth. Worse still, the tooth has a very deep cavity.

Patient   Will the pain disappear soon?

Dentist   It won't disappear immediately, but we can fix it. First I'll remove food debris between the wisdom tooth and the gum. I'll put a temporal cap on the cavity, and wash the gum. I'll give you an antiphlogistic, an antibiotic, and a painkiller.

Patient   How will the wisdom tooth be?

Dentist   If inflammation of the gum disappears, I'll pull out the wisdom tooth.

Patient   When will the inflammation disappear?

Dentist   The swelling may continue for another two or three days. But, hopefully the pain will stop by tomorrow. I'll be able to pull out the tooth next week. If you have time tomorrow or the day after tomorrow, drop by or please come and see me. I'll wash the tooth and the gum for you. Take care and see you again soon.

◯ TOOTH EXTRACTION

Patient   My crown came off when I was eating.

Dentist   Do you have the crown?

Patient   Yes, here it is.

Dentist   The crown fell out with part of the tooth.

Patient   Could you replace it?

Dentist   The cavity is too big, so it's difficult to replace, I have to pull out the tooth.

Patient   I see. That's bad news.

Dentist   I can't extract the tooth, because your gum is badly swollen. Today, I'll wash it out for you. And, I'll give you some medicine, there is an antibiotic, an antiphlogistic, and a painkiller. Please take them.

Next Visit

Dentist   Mrs. Carter, the swelling in your gum is much better. So I'll pull the tooth out. Have you had your blood pressure taken recently?

Patient   No. But, my blood pressure isn't high.

Dentist   Well, just in case I'll take it. It's one hundred and twenty-five over eighty. It's good. Have you ever experienced any excessive bleeding?

Patient   No.

Dentist   Are you receiving any medical treatment now?

Patient   No.

Dentist   Do you have any allergies to drugs or have you ever experienced any side effects, for

　　　　　副作用を経験したことがありますが？
患　者　いいえ．
歯科医　では麻酔をして，抜歯します．
患　者　抜いた後，痛みますか？
歯科医　そうですね，1〜2時間は麻酔が効いていますから，痛まないです．すぐに鎮痛剤や消炎剤を飲んでください．そうすれば，その後も痛まないでしょう．唇もしびれていますから，火傷に気をつけてください．明日は消毒に来てください．お大事に．

◯ 局麻時の不快症状とその対応

歯科医　どうぞ，お入りください．
患　者　こんにちは．
歯科医　どうなさいました？
患　者　下の奥歯が，すごく痛いのですが．
　　　　昨日の夜から何も食べられないのです．
歯科医　診てみましょう．口を開けてください．診察しますよ．痛みの原因となる歯が，何本かありますね．いつもは，どちらで治療されていますか？
患　者　実は，歯医者に行くのが怖くてもう何年も治療を受けていません．以前注射をしたときに，気分がわるくなったことがあったので，怖くて．そのとき，先生からは「麻酔薬が体質に合わずにアレルギーを起こしたんでしょう」と説明されました．
歯科医　そうですか．僕も治療されるのは，実はすごく怖いのですよ．なんとかよい方法で治療しましょうね．
　　　　まず，気分がわるくなったときの様子を教えてもらえますか？
患　者　注射をした後で，眩暈（めまい）がして，吐きそうになりました．
歯科医　息苦しさとかは，ありましたか？
患　者　ええ，胸が苦しくて，息がしにくい感じでした．
歯科医　蕁麻疹みたいなものは，そのとき出ましたか？
患　者　蕁麻疹はなかったと思います．
歯科医　わかりました．お話を伺った限りでは典型的なアレルギー反応ではなさそうですね．
患　者　治療して痛みは治りますか？
歯科医　安心してください．ちゃんと治療できますよ．ただ，痛いとか怖いとか，ストレスで気分がわるくなったりすることもあるので，できるだけ楽な気分で治療が受けられるようにしましょう．

ORAL SURGICAL TRETMANET & DENTAL ANESTHESIA

example to painkillers, penicillin, or injections?

Patient No.

Dentist OK, that's good. Now, I'll give you an anesthetic, and then pull out the tooth.

Patient Will I feel any pain after my tooth is pulled out?

Dentist Well, an anesthetic will last one or two hours. You won't feel any pain till then. Take a painkiller and an antiphlogistic when you get home. If you take these medicines, you won't feel any pain after that. Your lips might have a numb feeling, so be careful about burning your mouth. Please come to have it washed out tomorrow. Take care.

C DISCOMFORT EPISODE DURING DENTAL TREATMENT AND EFFECTIVE TREATMENT

Dentist Please, come in.

Patient Hello!

Dentist Hi! How are you doing?

Patient I have a terrible pain in my lower back tooth.
I haven't been able to eat since last night.

Dentist Let's have a look. Please open your mouth. I will check it. Hmm, there are several cavities here. Do you have any home dentist you can ask for treatment?

Patient Well, I haven't been to a dental clinic for several years. I'm really afraid of dentists. Previously, I have felt sick when I had a local anesthetic injection. Since then, I've avoided dentists. At that time, the dentist explained to me that I might have had an allergic reaction to the local anesthetic agent.

Dentist I see. I can tell you that I also don't like dentists, either. Let's try to make you feel more comfortable.
First, can you tell me about the previous episode?

Patient I felt a fainting-like symptom and I also had nausea.

Dentist Did you have any trouble in terms of breathing?

Patient Yes, I felt something blocking my breathing.

Dentist Did you have any kind of rash on the surface of your body?

Patient I don't think so.

Dentist OK. Your episode doesn't sound like a typical allergic reaction to me.

Patient Do you have any good ideas how to reduce this pain?

Dentist Any stress from pain perception, fear or anxiety may easily cause illness. Therefore I recommend special pain management during the treatment. It's called conscious sedation.

患者　　どんな方法ですか？痛くないですか？
歯科医　笑気吸入鎮静法という，ちょっと甘い匂いのする笑気という麻酔ガスを鼻から吸ってもらう方法と，静脈内鎮静法という，注射で少し眠くなる方法があります．どちらも気分がすごく楽になって，快適に歯科治療ができますよ．

患者　　はい．お願いします．
歯科医　じゃ，先ほどお話しした，笑気を吸ってみましょうか？これを鼻に装着しますから，鼻でゆっくり吸ってください．この方法は亜酸化窒素というガスを使った吸入鎮静法と呼ばれているものです．10分ぐらいで，だんだん楽な気分になってきますから．
　　　　（30%笑気吸入10分後）
歯科医　どうですか？
患者　　なんだか，体が暖かくなって，ふわふわした感じです．
歯科医　では，少し注射をして，しみるところにセメントを詰めるところまでやりましょう．どうですか？
患者　　大丈夫です．
歯科医　もうすこし麻酔をしますよ．（15分後）
　　　　大丈夫ですか？
患者　　はい，大丈夫です．
歯科医　少し，風をかけますよ．痛みますか？
患者　　いいえ．
歯科医　じゃあ，セメントを詰めて終わりますよ．笑気を切りますから，すぐ元に戻りますよ．
患者　　はい．

目が覚めてから
歯科医　いかがでしたか？注射も問題ないことが確認できたので，次回から，治療を開始しましょう．
患者　　アレルギーではないので，安心しました．今日はとっても楽に治療ができたので，また次回も笑気を使っていただけますか？
歯科医　わかりました．では，そうしましょう．副作用もなく，毎回使えます．腕の注射が怖くなければ，静脈内鎮静法はさらに快適な方法ですよ．実は，ここだけの話ですが，私も親知らずの抜歯治療のときは，この静脈内鎮静法で眠っている間にやってもらいました．ベンゾジアゼピンという鎮静剤を腕から静脈内注射します．私の患者たちもこちらの方が好きなようです．希望されるようであれば，次回の治療で，やってみますか？
患者　　はい．ぜひ，お願いします．

Patient   What is that? Is that painful?

Dentist   You will have a very comfortable feeling during this dental treatment. You can choose either inhalation sedation using nitrous oxide gas or intravenous sedation using administration of sedative agents. Do you want to start the dental treatment under conscious sedation today?

Patient   Yeah. Let's do it.

Dentist   OK. Let's try to use inhalation sedation. Can you put on this nasal mask and breathe slowly? You just breathe a sweet smelling gas through your nose. This aid treatment is called inhalation Conscious Sedation using Nitrous oxide gas. You will have a comfortable feeling within 10 minutes.

(Ten minutes later.)

Dentist   How do you feel?

Patient   I feel warm and floating.

Dentist   I will give you an initial treatment to reduce pain using a small amount of local anesthetic. How do you feel now?

Patient   I'm OK!

Dentist   I will give you an additional dose of local anesthesia. (Fifteen minutes later.) Are you OK?

Patient   Yeah, I am fine. I feel great.

Dentist   Do you feel any pain? (using air syringe)

Patient   No, nothing.

Dentist   That's good. Now, I'll put cement in the cavity. You will recover soon after cutting off the gas.

Patient   Thank you.

AFTER RECOVERING FROM THE SEDATION

Dentist   How was that? Fortunately, I don't see any problem using local anesthetic. I will start treatments from next time.

Patient   I am so happy not to be allergic to the anesthetic. Thanks for introducing me to conscious sedation. Can you use this management next time too?

Dentist   Sure. No problem. There are almost no major side effects. You can use this management technique every time. However, you can try also intravenous sedation if you don't mind injection in the arm. I can tell you that I always ask for this sedation during my dental treatment, for example extraction of wisdom teeth. You will receive benzodiazepine sedative drug via intravenous line in the arm. My patients seem to like it better, too. Do you want to be treated under intravenous sedation next time?

Patient   Yes, of course.

救急処置（一次救命処置）

局所麻酔薬を行った直後に，患者さんが，気分不快を訴えた．

患　者　先生，少し気分がわるいのですが．
歯科医　どんな感じですか？
患　者　吐き気がします．
歯科医　ちょっと脈を診ますね．少し脈が弱いかな？
患　者　先生，少し息苦しい感じがします．
歯科医　大丈夫ですか？血圧計とパルスオキシメータを装着しますよ．血圧を測りますね．上の血圧は90ぐらいですね．脈拍はすごく少ないね．40ぐらいかな？
衛生士　パルスオキシメータは93ぐらいですね．少し酸素を吸ってください．

患　者　先生，ちょっと眩暈がしてきました．
歯科医　大丈夫ですか？
患　者　（反応無し）
歯科医　○○さん！わかりますか？（肩を揺すって）
歯科医　衛生士の△△さん！患者の意識がないので，スタッフみんなを集めてください．すぐに救急車を呼んで，AEDを持ってきてください．
　　　　呼吸の確認をします．呼吸は分からないぐらい，すごく弱い．脈も触知できないぐらい，弱いので，一次救命処置（BLS）をします．みんな，手伝ってください．

アメリカの歯科事情7　－口腔外科専門医養成制度－

アメリカの口腔外科の専門医を養成するGraduate Program（大学院）では医師免許を取得するプログラムがあり，6～7年で口腔外科専門医と医師免許（内4年）を取得し，いわゆるダブルライセンスを取れるわけです．

BASIC LIFE SUPPORT (BLS)

Patient complain discomfort just after local anesthesia

Patient	Excuse me, Doctor? I don't feel well.
Dentist	Why? What happened?
Patient	I feel bad and nauseous.
Dentist	Let me check your pulse rate. Your pulse appears so weak.
Patient	I can't... I can't breath.
Dentist	Lady! Are you OK? I will take your blood pressure and pulse rate. I can see systolic blood pressure is around 90. The pulse rate seems extremely low around 40.
D.H.	The value of saturation was 93 in the room sir. I recommend you to use oxygen inhalation.
Patient	I feel dizzy and faint.
Dentist	Are you OK?
Patient	.... (No response any more)
Dentist	Lady! Are you OK? Can you hear me?
Dentist	Excuse me staff! A patient has fainted. There's no pulse. Can you ask everybody to help with support Basic Life Support? Can you call emergency and get AED. I will check respiration first. The respiration is very weak or the airway may be obstructed. I cannot confirm the pulse. I should start BLS algorism. Can you help me?

付録　国際的視野を持つ歯科医療人育成に必要な討議を英語で収録

Chairside Communication Discussion Questions

Lesson 1：

Has anybody ever spelled or pronounced your name wrong?

How did you feel?

What did you do about it?

Family name or first name, which would you prefer to be called?

When in doubt, which is the "proper" name to call patients（non-Japanese patients）?

How do you find a dentist?

Where do you go if you are new in town?

Lesson 2：

Are you embarrassed about how your teeth look?

Do you think the way patient's teeth look is becoming more important?

If so, what cultural changes have promoted this trend?

Lesson 3：

Do you think most patients take good care of their teeth?

Why do some patient's neglect taking care of their teeth?

Lesson 4：

When treating a patient who is under twelve, it's important that the child is calm, comfortable and informed. It's also just as important, if not more so, that the parents are calm, comfortable, and informed.

Do you agree?

What kind of culture gaps or language gaps can you expect?

Please consider, North American Cultures, and European Cultures, and Asian Cultures.

What can you do to encourage your patients to take responsibility for maintaining tooth care?

Lesson 5：

Recently, being sure patients are well informed is important, but what information is too much?

What kind of small talk is appropriate and what kind of small talk is inappropriate? Please consider the age of the patients.

Lesson 6：

Discuss in what cases and why patients find it difficult making choices about tooth care.

What are some ways that dentists can help make decision making easier for patients.

In another words, in what ways can dentists increase patient's autonomy.

What are some ways that dental professionals could improve the decision making resources for their patients?

Lesson 7：

Following basic instructions is often the most important improvements that patients can make in the health of their teeth.

Review some basic instructions for tooth brushing, caring for dentures etc.

Lesson 8：

The general health of patients is a big factor to consider.

What health problems would be especially important for dentists to take into consideration and why? Resulting from stress.

Lesson 9：

Describe the 3 kinds of medication that are usually prescribed together to treat an abscess, an infection, and an extraction?

What cautions should patients take when they are on prescribed medication?

Lesson 10：

The aging population in Japan has "special" needs that dentists will have to accommodate.

Discuss the nature of these needs and in what ways dentists can equip themselves to deal with them.

With a partner, do some role plays of a dentist explaining about how to do an endoscope and a patient who is learning about an endoscope.

Lesson 11：

What are some worst "nightmare scenarios" that dentists might have to face and what are the best ways to handle them?

Discuss typical "monster patients" and the most effective way to deal with them.

※本書は2011年4月に「チェアーサイドの歯科英会話─外国人患者が診療所を訪れたら─ CD-ROM付」として発行されたものを，内容は発行時のまま，音声データをCDではなく，小社WEBサイトを通じて提供する形式に変更したうえで，再発行したものです．

チェアーサイドの歯科英会話
─外国人患者が診療所を訪れたら─
音声DL付　　　　　　　　　　　　　　ISBN 978-4-263-42338-7

2025年7月5日　第1版第1刷発行

　　　　　監　修　加　藤　有　三
　　　　　発行者　白　石　泰　夫
　　　　　発行所　医歯薬出版株式会社

〒113-8612　東京都文京区本駒込1-7-10
TEL．（03）5395-7638（編集）・7630（販売）
FAX．（03）5395-7639（編集）・7633（販売）
https://www.ishiyaku.co.jp/
郵便振替番号　00190-5-13816

乱丁，落丁の際はお取り替えいたします　　印刷・木元省美堂／製本・愛千製本所
Ⓒ Ishiyaku Publishers, Inc., 2025. Printed in Japan

本書の複製権・翻訳権・翻案権・上映権・譲渡権・貸与権・公衆送信権（送信可能化権を含む）・口述権は，医歯薬出版㈱が保有します．
本書を無断で複製する行為（コピー，スキャン，デジタルデータ化など）は，「私的使用のための複製」などの著作権法上の限られた例外を除き禁じられています．また私的使用に該当する場合であっても，請負業者等の第三者に依頼し上記の行為を行うことは違法となります．

JCOPY ＜出版者著作権管理機構　委託出版物＞
本書をコピーやスキャン等により複製される場合は，そのつど事前に出版者著作権管理機構（電話03-5244-5088，FAX 03-5244-5089，e-mail：info@jcopy.or.jp）の許諾を得てください．

.